James Hunt receives a helping hand from pop group Glamourpuss at Brands Hatch, July 1976

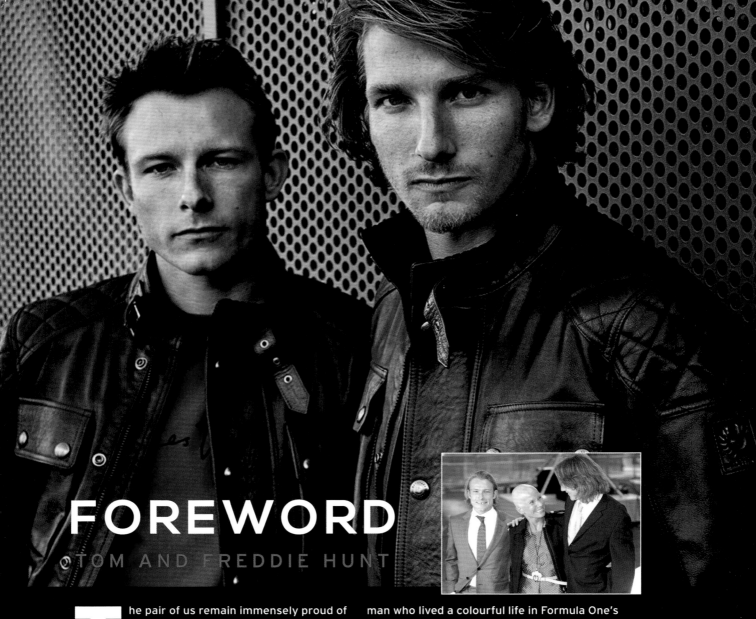

FOREWORD
TOM AND FREDDIE HUNT

The pair of us remain immensely proud of our father for his achievements 40 years ago.

Of course, unfortunately, he is not around to celebrate his momentous effort in that season but the interest and excitement that 1976 still generates remains extraordinary.

Dad lived an incredible life and was the toast of the British sporting public during a decade where Formula One really captured the nation's imagination.

Nobody was more responsible for that than dad as his character, enthusiasm and charisma helped bring the sport to life. What is clear – from the interviews in this special publication and beyond – is that he was a complete one-off; a colourful man who lived a colourful life in Formula One's most colourful era.

His courage, openness, talent and dedication continue to impress and inspire us and we are sure you will relish the story of dad's incredible rivalry with Niki Lauda and his skill and bravery.

James Hunt was a true British champion.

But, above all, he was dad – simply dad.

We hope you enjoy reliving his extraordinary life, on and off the track.

We would also like to dedicate this souvenir to our mum, Sarah, who sadly passed away in 2014.

Along with dad, she helped provide a wonderfully stable and loving upbringing and we miss her tremendously.

Tom and Freddie are wearing items from the James Hunt 40th anniversary collection, by Belstaff

CONTENTS

THANKS TO: DERICK ALLSOP, MURRAY WALKER, CHRIS JONES, SALLY JONES, JOHN RICHARDSON, TOM HUNT, FREDDIE HUNT, ADAM ACWORTH AND THE SANTARA GROUP
PHOTO CREDIT: TONY WOOLLISCROFT, JOHN TOWNSEND/WWW.F1PICTURES.COM, CORBIS IMAGES, PRESS ASSOCIATION, MIRRORPIX
PRODUCED BY TRINITY MIRROR SPORT MEDIA, PO BOX 48, LIVERPOOL, L69 3EB
ISBN 9781910335383
MANAGING DIRECTOR: STEVE HANRAHAN
COMMERCIAL DIRECTOR: WILL BEEDLES
EXECUTIVE ART EDITOR: RICK COOKE
EXECUTIVE EDITOR: PAUL DOVE
WRITER: CHRIS BRERETON
SUB-EDITOR: GARY GILLILAND
DESIGN & PRODUCTION: BEN RENSHAW, GLEN HIND, TOM ROGERS
PRINTED BY: WILLIAM GIBBONS

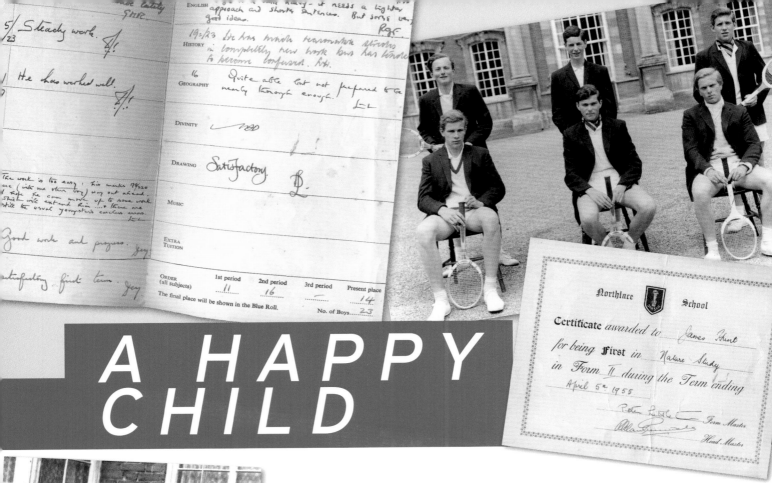

A HAPPY CHILD

Northlace School

Certificate awarded to James Hunt
for being First in Nature Study
in Form II during the Term ending
April 5th 1955

TOP: One of Hunt's school reports show he was a good student – but sport was always his first love

ABOVE: Hunt, aged around four, standing behind, at Tabor Court in 1951. Sally is on the left on the wall

RIGHT: The whole Hunt family taken at Grange Road in 1962. Back row (l to r) James, Sally, Peter. Front row (l to r) Wallis with David on his lap, Tim, Sue with Georgina on her lap

J ames Simon Wallis Hunt seemed determined to make an impact on the world from the very start.

Hunt, born on August 29, 1947, was a boisterous baby, prone to energetic outbursts which involved trying to wrestle himself free of his pram and cot at every opportunity and he frequently drove parents Sue and Wallis to distraction.

Adored distraction, of course.

Hunt was one of six children to the couple, with Sally being the eldest, then James, before Peter, Timothy, David and Georgina all followed.

"James was a delightful brother," Sally said. "He was always very lively, good company; he always wanted to get his own way – and made a song and dance about it if he didn't – but he was always very focused and determined when he put his mind to it."

Hunt started life in a flat in Tabor Court, Cheam, on the London-Surrey border, until the expanding size of the family prompted several moves, first to Meadowside Road, a four-bedroomed detached in Cheam, then to a huge Victorian house in Grange Road, Sutton – where David and Georgina were born – and then a final move to The Drive, Belmont.

Hunt's childhood was full of the usual scrapes and bumps and bruises that accompany the lives of all headstrong young men and he was not scared of throwing his weight around on his younger brothers, either.

Peter, in particular, seems to have borne most of his big brother's brunt, needing hospital treatment on one occasion when James decided to hit him with a spade.

He would not be the last person to be on the wrong end of James's temper in the

years to come...

Hunt began his schooling at Ambleside, a prep school in Cheam, and the school reports show he was a better than average student - despite hating virtually every second of it.

"He was happier playing sport than academic stuff, but he was very bright," Sally recalls.

"My main memory of Ambleside is when he was in nursery and I would've been in what is now called the Reception class. If he was being a problem - having a strop - I'd be summoned upstairs to calm him down. I'm not sure how much use I was though!"

After Ambleside he went to another prep school in Hastings where, again, he combined a decent level of academic interest with a loathing of the place before finally attending Wellington College, the prestigious public school in Berkshire.

Hunt found an outlet for his school frustrations in sport. In fact, he excelled at virtually everything he tried, including tennis (including playing at Junior Wimbledon), squash and cross-country running.

Hunt took sport and competing extremely seriously - he was extremely driven and wanted to win.

Always, always, win.

It was a sign of what was to come in his later life.

As was his love of budgies. As incongruous as that might sound, the young James - already smoking, already testing authority, already showing sporting prowess - also had a deep love of pets, animals and nature in general.

He was never happier than when running around with Ricky, the Hunt family's beloved black Labrador, and when he was given a budgerigar as a gift, it prompted a lifelong affection for breeding the birds.

At Wellington, Hunt thought seriously about becoming a doctor but, again,

playing sport - and the trumpet - were his main loves and he excelled at both.

The austere surroundings of Wellington helped forge Hunt's individualistic, headstrong character even further. If you wanted something in life, then you had to go and get it for yourself.

Hunt was more than happy for this to be the case.

And as he - literally - careered and crashed his way through his teenage years, a young Hunt, on the cusp of adulthood, was to have a moment that would change his career plans - and life - for ever.

Northlace School

Certificate *awarded to* James Hunt *for being* **First** *in* Reading *in* Form I *during the term ending* Christmas 1954

K. M. Hudson   Form Master

J. Hunt B.A. Head Master

Hunt looks to
see if he's made
the papers

FROM SCHOOL TO SPEED

James was on the verge of a career in medicine, but a day out at Silverstone set him on a different path altogether...

I T happened to me in an instant," James Hunt once explained, when discussing how he ended up choosing speed over surgery.

"I was destined for medicine, purely by a process of elimination, because it was the least of the evils in the unimaginative list of careers you were given at school."

Yet, that all changed when Hunt visited Silverstone, aged 18, to watch an August Bank Holiday event involving Minis.

"It was only a club race," Hunt said. "But I thought, 'This is pretty bloody good.'"

Almost overnight, Hunt decided he would start driving and competing in a Mini he would build himself.

And he always claimed that despite those humble beginnings, his eye was always on the glory of winning the Formula One World Championship.

"I am a competitor," he explained. "I'm ambitious and I always tried to be the best in whatever sport I took on, so Formula One had to be the target right from the start of my racing career."

Or, to put it another way, as he did in an interview with Penthouse in 1976: "There's no point being a ******. Do something properly or don't bother."

Hunt certainly had plans to do it properly, if slightly eccentrically.

"I needed money fast and I offered my old man a deal," he said. "It would have cost him five grand to put me through medical school but as I wasn't going, I'd settle for £2,500 cash. He told me to get ******!"

Despite virtually no money, Hunt built his Mini bit by bit, searching the south of England for salvageable scraps.

A variety of jobs, including being a cleaner at the Royal Marsden Hospital, came and went as he did whatever it took to (literally) fuel his new found passion.

"Once he decided racing was for him, there was no stopping him," Sally Jones, James's sister, said.

Hunt's parents were not overly keen on his new career path, especially as most weekends seemed to involve a prang or two, but Hunt would not be deterred and the family garage soon became covered in bits of engine and exhaust, seats and spark plugs.

By 1967, Hunt's Mini was ready for action. Or maybe not.

The list of reasons why his creation would not get past the safety scrutineer at his first proposed race at Snetterton, Norfolk, sounds like it could run into the hundreds.

Was it the deckchair seat, nabbed from the Hunts' front garden and bolted down?

Or was it the lack of windows?

Hunt's car never even got close to the tarmac, but he refused to give up and he returned home with plans to do all it took to get his car out on the track.

Eventually, Hunt managed this but, unfortunately for him, motor racing

ABOVE: Hunt was always supremely focused once he sat in the cockpit

OPPOSITE: A March team press release from 1971 outlining Hunt's staggered progression through feeder formulas

rewards competency rather than enthusiasm and the Mini was a constant headache – breaking down, spewing oil and leaving him going nowhere quickly, or not so quickly, as the case may be.

Yet, again, he would not be put off.

After more desperate financial wranglings, Hunt saw his chance in 1968 in the Formula Ford class, a recently designed format that saw races up and down the country.

Hunt bought himself a chassis as well as an engine and again set about showing the country's race fans that he could be the real deal.

Not even Hunt would claim that the 1968 season was an overriding success, but all the ingredients for his future glory were on display.

He was tenacious – often going without hotel rooms in order to push all his finances in the direction of his car rather than his own well-being – he was fast (when his car allowed him to be) and he was aggressive.

Sometimes perhaps too aggressive.

At Oulton Park during that season, Hunt wiped out his new car in a crash that could easily have claimed his life.

After finding himself stuck behind someone in trouble, Hunt tried to avoid hitting the car but succeeded only in taking off at speed, eventually coming to a stop when his car sank to the bottom of a lake after careering through an advertising board.

Hunt somehow emerged virtually unscathed, although the blood smeared across his face gave a hint of how close he could have come to a far worse ending.

> **"I AM AMBITIOUS AND I ALWAYS TRIED TO BE THE BEST IN WHATEVER SPORT I TOOK ON, SO FORMULA ONE HAD TO BE THE TARGET RIGHT FROM THE START OF MY RACING CAREER"**

As Hunt's experience and know-how grew in the almost non-stop Formula Ford roadshow over the next few seasons, he finally started becoming more recognised, so much so that a move to Formula Three seemed like the natural next step.

Finally, Hunt seemed to be ascending the ladder. Those hours of self-taught mechanic work, unfashionable jobs and parsimonious living were starting to pay off.

By this stage, Hunt's well-known propensity to vomit extensively before a race was well developed. The nerves he felt were the nerves of a man desperate to win – but also one who knew how close to the edge he was having to push himself to try and be successful.

The danger of motor racing in the early 1970s looks almost insane from the thankfully safer haven of today's sport and yet, time and time again, Hunt got into a car and would shake with adrenaline.

He overcame it all though and continued to inch his way forward, even if times were equally as tough in Formula Three – and then Formula Two – as they were in his earlier, more barren years.

Hunt himself certainly had no rose-tinted view of his time trying to climb the motor racing ladder, especially as the early 1970s were marred by the unfortunate moniker of "Hunt the Shunt" due to the amount of crashes and incidents he found himself in.

"It was terrible, the lowest point in my life," he told Penthouse. "I got into Formula Three racing and things went from bad to worse – bad cars, bad everything. Broke. I had to knock on people's doors for sponsorship. They all thought I was an amiable nutter, obsessed with racing. This carried on for about three awful years."

After competing in Formula Three in a Brabham BT21 and March 693, Hunt's 1970 season saw him change to a Lotus 59 with decent results.

Yet, three accidents that season were joined by seven the season after and then a further four in 1972, during which time he moved to Formula Two, again with little notable success.

It seemed that no matter how Hunt tried to compete, he just would not get his big break.

Or would he?

PRESS   INFORMATION

JAMES HUNT TO DRIVE WORKS MARCH IN FORMULA 3

Drives also in Formula 2

Contrary to popular expectation James Hunt has decided to stay in Formula 3 for 1971 and has signed for the March team.   His expected entry into Formula 2 is not being delayed because although he will be concentrating on Formula 3 he will be doing as many Formula 2 races as possible when his other commitments allow.

With so many drivers decrying the dangers of Formula 3 James' decision may come as a surprise to many that he did not take the chance to go into Formula 2 full time – he explained it like this : "My immediate ambition is to get into Formula 1 and I see F3 as being the best way to place myself on view to F1 team managers.   It is not that I like the dangers of F3, I don't, but I believe it is possible to stay out of trouble if you drive intelligently.   Last year I learnt a terrific amount in Formula 3 and next year I intend to capitalise on it by winning a lot of races.   It is significant to me that all the past "kings" of F3 are now Grand Prix drivers - last year there was no "king" just 3 or 4 "princes" in F3 and I intend to put that right for next season by establishing myself as the "king" which I feel, will give me far more chance of getting straight into Formula 1 than having a good Formula 2 season would.

However, I will be doing F2 because I need all the experience I can get and of course it will give me the much needed chance to race against graded drivers."

To aid these plans to fruition James has just signed for March Engineering for the 1971 season and he is looking forward to his new association.   He says that he spent a very happy season with Lotus Components and has parted with them on good terms.   He will be campaigning the works 713 Formula 3 car with the main goal being the much-rumoured European Formula 3 Championship, and he will be driving a 712 in Formula 2 races although details of this will not be announced just yet.

For details of the Formula 3 team see the Press Kit attached.
Any other information please contact :
John Hogan,
145 East Hill,
London SW18.
Telephone 01-262 3424 (Day)
           01-874 1809 (Evenings)

1 January 1971

HESKETH
RACING
AUTHORISED
CALLERS
ONLY

Lord Hesketh keeps Hunt
company on the Hesketh 308. The
duo helped change the world of
Formula One

HUNT AND HESKETH

When Lord Hesketh needed a new driver and James needed a new challenge, the circumstances were perfectly set up to provide Formula One with one of its most captivating stories...

There are many racing teams which have slipped into history unnoticed, disbanded and unloved.

For every Red Bull or Renault, every McLaren or Mercedes, there are endless Lambos and Lancias, McGuires and Milanos.

However, Hesketh Racing did more than enough to ensure that its attempts to crack Formula One have been remembered longer, and more fondly, than most.

Sometimes in life, events conspire and the planets align just so, and that was the case with Hesketh Racing and James Hunt.

The two were a perfect match, meeting at the perfect time under the perfect circumstances.

By 1972, after years struggling in motor racing's backwaters, Hunt seemed to be out of cash, out of luck and out of time.

All his efforts in getting noticed, getting sponsorship and forging ahead seemed to be going to waste. "Hunt the Shunt" was going nowhere quickly.

And then Hesketh saved the day.

The "Hesketh" after whom the team was named was in fact Thomas Alexander Fermor-Hesketh, a real-life Baron – a 22-year-old member of the British aristocracy who was keen on fast cars and an even faster lifestyle.

Lord Hesketh loved having fun and enjoyed the experiences that came with being a young man to whom all of society's doors were well and truly open.

Does that remind you of anybody? Hesketh and Anthony "Bubbles" Horsley – the team manager and sometime driver – were unconventional, uninterested in the polite niceties of motor racing, rebellious and willing to mix things up.

Forays into Formula Three, with Horsley driving, had been generally unsuccessful and Hesketh's future seemed as uncertain

James with girlfriend Suzy Miller, who is wearing a Hesketh teddy logo T-shirt, Brands Hatch, July 1974

> **MY CAREER HAD REALLY STAGNATED BADLY. IT WAS TIME TO DO SOMETHING DIFFERENT AND AT THAT MOMENT, FORTUNATELY FOR ME, HESKETH RACING DECIDED TO COME AND TALK TO ME**

as Hunt's, but both persevered and realised they needed the other.

"My career had really stagnated badly," Hunt said. "It was time to do something different and at that moment, fortunately for me, Hesketh Racing decided to come and talk to me.

"They had already approached me in the winter without revealing who they were because they were a new team. They were also having a bit of a disaster.

"The next race was at Chimay in Belgium and somebody had just lent me a car to drive there.

"I decided that as I'd got nothing else I'd go and talk to the Hesketh team. Bubbles

Hesketh Racing was about driving fast - and living faster. Hunt fitted in perfectly, but he also recognised that his big opportunity to finally forge a career in Formula One had only just begun

and I bumped into each other in the middle of this field in Belgium. We'd both set off to see each other at the same time."

Hunt could not have fitted in better and not for nothing did he label Hesketh "The Good Lord" as there was no doubt Hesketh had opened the door to glory, glamour and girls.

The Formula One outsiders wanted to plough their own furrow as Lord Hesketh invested money in a state-of-the-art yacht rather than a back-up car and the blonde, buxom entourage that followed the Hesketh Racing bus around the globe created headlines wherever it went.

"Alexander would bring his mates and they'd have a huge party, but behind the smokescreen – because it was very difficult to see through it – the team were very serious and professional," Hunt said.

"The combination of fun and seriousness suited me. When I was concentrating on the race it didn't interfere or bother me having all that fun around.

"They were a jolly nice crowd and after the race, when it was time to stop work, I was able to enjoy the party."

The initial plan for Hesketh Racing was to race in both Formula One and Formula Two in the 1973 season, but in the end Lord Hesketh decided to go for broke, throwing

Hunt's Hesketh team in 1974, from left to right: Harvey Postlethwaite (designer), Anthony "Bubbles" Horsley, Hunt and Lord Hesketh

Hunt was always a bundle of nervous energy at a racetrack

Impressing on his way to fourth place in the Hesketh Racing March 731 during the British Grand Prix at Silverstone in 1973

his weight behind an all-out assault on Formula One.

That decision might have looked recklessly in keeping with the cigarettes, smiles, sex and champagne, but behind all that lay Hunt, a man destined and determined to take his big opportunity.

It was now time for Hunt to produce on the track under the kind of scrutiny and pressure that had never existed before.

Yet nobody, least of all Hunt, ever had any concerns about his mental or physical ability to withstand the new rigours he was about to endure.

"James was the most competitive

> **JAMES HAD TO WIN AT WHATEVER IT WAS HE WAS TAKING PART IN. HE REALLY LUCKED OUT WHEN HE JOINED HESKETH**

man I've ever met," Chris Jones, one of his closest friends, said. "James had to win at whatever it was he was taking part in.

"He really lucked out when he joined Hesketh – I don't know what he would have done without it – but there was no doubt that he would do everything he could to seize the opportunity."

Hunt had arrived.

But could he deliver?

Few got close to beating Hunt on the squash court and he could probably have represented his country at that, or tennis, if motor racing had not captured his imagination instead

CAR-PE DIEM

Hunt was desperate to seize the day – and seize his chance to create history with Hesketh...

HUNT immediately showed his desire to grab headlines for Hesketh Racing for his prowess in the car rather than the fun had away from the track.

At the 1973 Race of Champions at Brands Hatch, a 40 lap non-championship race featuring a plethora of different vehicles, he started 13th on the grid but ended up sealing third place in a Surtees, a superb performance by both man and machine.

Hunt's Formula One debut followed shortly after that March day at the Monaco Grand Prix.

For both Hunt and the Hesketh team, it seemed particularly apt for him to make his debut at the epicentre of Formula One's glitz and glamour, complete with a new car – the March 731.

Hunt's nerves before the race – a constant feature throughout his career – saw him being violently sick and he wrestled hard to keep his new, far more powerful car under full control throughout the gruelling afternoon's work.

Eventually, Jackie Stewart took the chequered flag, but Hunt was nowhere to be seen after engine trouble meant he had to retire.

It had been an important lesson, though, in what it takes to operate at the highest level and Hunt was no longer under any illusions about just how tough Formula One was.

The dawning realisation of how difficult it would be to muscle his way onto the podium did not prevent him from partying hard in Monaco along with Lord Hesketh, "Bubbles" Horsley and the rest of the Hesketh team as they announced their arrival in Formula One – come win or lose – in style.

Hunt performed even better in his next race, the France Grand Prix, picking up his first ever point with a sixth-place finish.

Cue more celebrations.

After finishing fourth at the British Grand Prix on July 14, Hunt managed to get his first podium finish in the race that followed, the Dutch Grand Prix, just over a fortnight later.

It was a superb performance and an indicator to the rest of the field that he appeared to be the coming man.

Nobody was laughing about Hesketh Racing any more.

After failing to finish in Austria and not even starting in Italy due to a practice accident, Hunt's final two races of the 1973 season saw him finish seventh in Canada and then second in the United States.

> ## "AT ZANDVOORT, I LAID TO REST THE GHOST COMPLETELY BECAUSE I COULDN'T HAVE HAD GREATER PRESSURE THAN I HAD IN THAT RACE. IT WAS MY COMING OF AGE"

ABOVE: Hunt's marriage to Suzy Miller in 1974

From just seven Grand Prix starts, Hunt finished the season in eighth place with 14 points.

Hunt began 1974 in even better form, brilliantly winning the BRDC International Trophy held at Silverstone on April 7.

After starting on pole, he conceded the lead to Ronnie Peterson but fought back wonderfully and overtook him towards the end with a superb piece of driving that enabled him to finish first.

That seemed to herald a promising season, but the 1974 Formula One season turned out to be a steep learning curve for Hunt.

Four accidents (the "Hunt the Shunt" nickname refused to die completely) and only three podium finishes – in Sweden, Austria and the USA – meant he finished the season with 15 points and, again, in eighth position in the World Championship standings.

However, he had raced 15 times, rather than the mere seven the season before.

That was clearly a disappointing return for Hunt and Hesketh – particularly as they had also introduced their own car during the season, switching from a March 731 to a Hesketh 308. However, the season was soon forgotten when Hunt announced he was to get married.

Hunt had met Suzy Miller in Spain – he had moved to the Costa del Sol in order to avoid some steep British government tax rates – and she had quickly become part of the Hesketh entourage.

A blonde, beautiful model, Suzy more than fitted into the archetypal mould for Hunt, who had become an international playboy with a rapidly growing reputation that he never did anything to deflect or deny.

As soon as the 1974 season was over, Hunt and Miller booked Brompton Oratory

Winner for Susy

MOTOR racing ace James Hunt is to marry former model Susy Miller. The couple, pictured above, announced their engagement in London yesterday. They met just twelve weeks ago in southern Spain, where they both live. It was a brief encounter at a tennis club. But Hunt, star of Britain's Hesketh grand prix team, knew he was on the right track.

After a few dates, he popped the question over lunch. Susy said Yes. And now the couple, both 26, plan a London wedding in October.

Picture: ALISDAIR MACDONALD.

in London for their wedding, attended by the great and good of Formula One and beyond.

Despite some serious and long-lasting second thoughts on marriage, Hunt seemed happy enough and when the 1975 season arrived Hesketh Racing attacked it with their customary gusto.

Yet, despite their enthusiasm, Hunt failed to make any real inroads in the standings despite a second-place finish at the Argentine Grand Prix.

Accidents in Spain and Monaco fuelled his outrage – Hunt was not to be messed with immediately after a collision as his

notorious temper could often overflow – and consecutive retirements at Belgium and Sweden left the 1975 season on a knife-edge.

June 22, 1975, changed all that.

Racing in the Dutch Grand Prix at Zandvoort, Hunt brilliantly judged the drying conditions to come in for an early pit stop to change to slick tyres ahead of the rest of the field. Although he rejoined the race well out of contention, he was soon in the lead as car after car followed his earlier example.

Hunt had 60 laps to keep his nerve, his control and guide the Hesketh 308 home.

Chasing him was a certain Niki Lauda and for those 60 long, long laps the two engaged in one of the all-time great Formula One battles.

Lauda did everything to pass, Hunt did everything to keep him at bay.

The pair of them thrashed their engines to the very limit and drove themselves to the edge of what is possible, both physically and mentally.

In the pits, every member of the Hesketh Racing team counted down the laps, barely able to believe that Hunt could hold off the Austrian genius behind him.

But hold him off he did, Hunt crossing the line barely a second ahead of Lauda to record his first Grand Prix victory.

"It was my coming of age," Hunt said. "It was both exciting and important for me. It rounded off my education. On three occasions before then I'd seen the chance to win a Grand Prix and panicked, got overexcited and made a mistake.

"At Zandvoort, I laid to rest the ghost completely because I couldn't have had greater pressure than I had in that race."

By this stage of the season, Hunt had transformed into Formula One's most photogenic, exciting and unpredictable star.

He seemed the epitome of 1970s glamour and he often shocked and thrilled his fans by his manner and action off the track as much as on it.

"After a race, we'd often pitch tents and a caravan or two," Chris Jones said.

"After the race, he would spend the night in the tent. It was great. When we ran out of booze, James would get up and go and knock on these other tents that were around. He'd say, 'James Hunt here, do you have any spare booze?'

"Well, you can imagine the reaction. They would open the door and if they had a camera they would say, 'Talk us through the last few laps and we will give you some beer.' James would do as they asked and then get the spare beer. Can you imagine that now!

"When we were leaving Brands one

time, there was a kid with a broken arm and as we were in a traffic jam and going nowhere James got out of the car, signed the kid's arm and just chatted with everybody.

"He loved doing that, just being relaxed with the people, especially those he had grown up with."

Hunt's fantastic win in Holland was to prove to be the pinnacle moment of his time with Hesketh.

Second in the French and Austrian Grands Prix helped Hunt secure fourth place in the World Championship standings with 33 points and there was no doubt his career had taken huge leaps forward.

However, significant changes were around the corner.

By the end of the 1975 season, the huge cost of funding the Hesketh team had become too much.

The fact the team had no dominant sponsor had not helped and before too long Hunt and Hesketh prepared to go their separate ways.

Again, Hunt was in desperate need of a

racing team who, in turn, were in desperate need for a driver.

"In the end, there was no sponsor and no money," Hunt lamented.

"I stuck it out until the November and, luckily, a top drive became available at that rather strange time of year."

The "top drive" he was referring to was at McLaren.

Emerson Fittipaldi had left the team at short notice, leaving a gaping hole in McLaren's plans for the 1976 season.

Once again, Hunt had found the slice of fortune he needed to keep his career on track.

As Hunt was clearly Formula One's most promising driver and with McLaren eager to get a serious contender in their car, it was another wise decision by all parties to approach each other.

Soon enough, the deal was done.

The white of Hesketh Racing was to be replaced by the red of McLaren.

The path was set for the most amazing Formula One season of them all.

RIGHT: Hunt was famous – or infamous – for the risque badges on his Hesketh racesuit. He had another that read: 'Sex: Breakfast of Champions'

BELOW: James stands triumphant at Zandvoort in 1975 ahead of Niki Lauda (left) and Clay Regazzoni (right). More thrilling duels were to follow shortly

RIGHT TIME, RIGHT PLACE

In this exclusive interview, Lord Hesketh explains how he recruited James and their remarkable journey together

Lord Hesketh's place in motor racing history is well secured. As the owner of Hesketh Racing, his foray into Formula One remains one of the sport's most remarkable tales and although four decades have passed since his association with James Hunt, he remains as outspoken now as he did when Hesketh Racing first tipped the sport's accepted rules and etiquette upside down.

History may have judged Lord Hesketh's involvement in the sport with a wry smile; fuelled by plenty of images of Hunt, Hesketh and Anthony "Bubbles" Horsley in party mode. However, as Hunt himself said, Hesketh Racing was deadly serious when it came to trying to become an established Formula One force.

"There's nothing in the world that makes you want to succeed as much as other people not taking you seriously," Lord Hesketh said.

"Everyone said, 'All Hunt's done is crash some cars in some pretty lowly Formulas – they are amateurs, we are professionals and they don't know what they're doing.' That was all we needed. That is the greatest encouragement you can give to anyone. There was no magic to it."

As mentioned elsewhere, Hunt's rise into a Formula One competitive car was extremely fortunate and fast, but Lord Hesketh remembers a driver who was well equipped with getting to grips with the demands placed upon him.

Hunt's first Grand Prix – racing the March 731 at Monaco in 1973 – is a case in point. Hunt was so wet behind the ears it was a miracle his helmet did not steam up. Yet, he handled the power, pressure and pace of his car brilliantly.

"James was a very good learner," Lord Hesketh explained. "He was in awe of nobody because once you get in the car it is all about the machine.

"The first car we had was a March 731. Harvey Postlethwaite was the No.2 engineer at March and when I bought the car from March I took him at the same time.

"James qualified for Monaco and I'd be amazed if he'd had 500 miles in Formula

Two previously, including testing. That really was a remarkable achievement.

"He was running in sixth until the car let him down and then he went to France and picked up a point. Some people spend years trying to get one point."

Lord Hesketh also believes that his first foray into racing at the highest level gave Hunt some sobering insights into what was required if he was going to become one of the world's best.

"James couldn't get out of the car after Monaco," he said. "He was an incredibly fit guy but he lost an enormous amount of weight – something like eight pounds – and he was too exhausted to get out of the car on his own.

"He had to go into a training regime and I think that was probably the biggest change he had to make. He realised that he had to be a different gear fitter. Not just a week or two in the gym, but a consistent programme of getting himself up to where he wanted to be."

The improvements both Hesketh's mechanics and Hunt made during their time together soon ensured they were shown respect by other teams in the pit lane yet, to everybody's frustration, a first Formula One victory remained elusive until Hunt turned up at the Dutch Grand Prix in 1975.

His outstanding performance in holding off Lauda for the win is clearly and

indelibly imprinted on Lord Hesketh's mind.

"Zandvoort was part of a frustrating season because we led in five Grands Prix but some unfortunate incidents had deprived us of the chequered flag," he said.

"It was beautiful sunshine on Friday and Saturday but it rained on Sunday morning. We shouldn't have won the race, but we did because we had some luck that went our way.

"The first was that we had another car coming, but Harvey had gone home. He was at Silverstone testing, so we didn't know what to do with the wings and the settings on the car. We had to leave it as it

was and, fortunately, it turned out to be great.

"The second was that during the race James realised there was a dry line on the middle of the track. He had also worked this out at Monaco earlier in the season. You hear commentators now bore on about it, but it was invented by James.

"He realised that even if the track looked soaking wet, if you stuck to that line you could put on slicks and drive faster.

"At Monaco, he came in way ahead of anyone else - unfortunately, we screwed up the pit stop - but in Holland he did it again. He swept into the pit lane early in the race and everybody was amazed by this. In he came and out he went on slicks to the back of the field.

"But the track slowly dried out and, of course, everybody else came in. The two Ferraris came in and Niki recognised what James had done. By this time James was out in front."

Hunt had a long, lonely drive ahead as his crew sat waiting to see if their driver had managed to hold off Lauda & Co.

"At Zandvoort there is a very, very long straight that comes all the way down and then a hairpin that goes around the sand dunes and then comes out at the end of that straight," Lord Hesketh added.

"Each time you could see this white blob coming off the turn and, to start with, there was quite a long gap. But then, slowly, the white blob was joined by a red one... and then another red one. Niki got closer and closer and closer and eventually, on the last three or four laps, Niki was very close to getting under James's wing.

"Anyhow, he was quick enough to hang on and he discovered an extra something, so the order stood and it brought great joy, but more so a sense of huge relief."

Surprisingly, Lord Hesketh is more effusive when he recalls Hunt's BRDC International Trophy victory at Silverstone in 1974.

It was Hesketh Racing's first success and, despite being a non-championship race, the manner of Hunt's performance, chasing Ronnie Peterson down before passing him with a wonderfully bold move late on, provokes bigger smiles than the Dutch victory.

"That first win was more exciting because he started on pole position but came round after the first lap in about 17th place," he said.

"He then had to carve his way back into contention. He finally overtook Peterson with two wheels on the grass at 160mph. After winning like that, nothing else is ever going to be the same."

After the 1975 season, nothing was indeed the same.

Hunt left for McLaren and Lord Hesketh's involvement in Hesketh Racing came to an end.

Hunt, and the world, had moved on. Yet the charisma, will to win and enthusiasm Hesketh Racing brought to Formula One helped give the sport more colour and character.

"It was more fun and people didn't take themselves as seriously," Lord Hesketh said. "It was a different age and it's very hard to judge. There were far less regulations and it was a different time.

"It's a different business in every shape and form these days. It's changed so much – some of it can be defined and some cannot be."

As for his relationship with Hunt and what the pair had done for each other, Lord Hesketh is unequivocal.

He said: "Without him, the team would never have got where we got to. Without the team, James would never have got his opportunity.

"Without those two phenomena coming together, it wouldn't have existed. I leave it to others to decide whether that was for the betterment of racing."

It was Lord Hesketh, it was.

James Hunt's relationship with his dog Oscar was one of the most important in his life. Here he is putting his Alsatian through his paces on a beach in Marbella in May 1979

1976

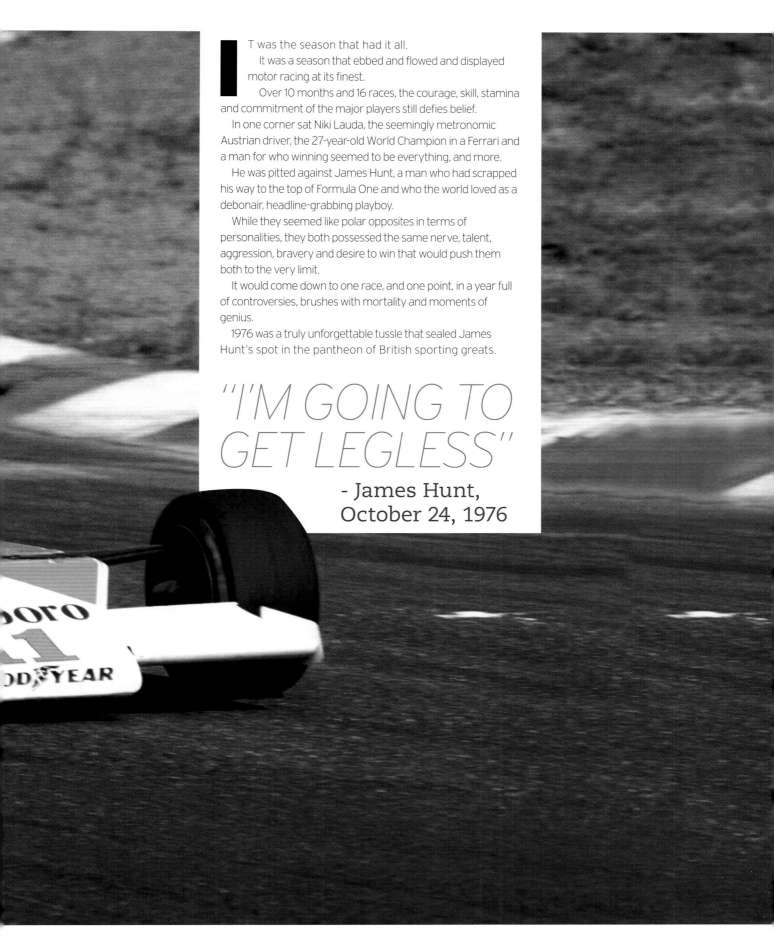

IT was the season that had it all.

It was a season that ebbed and flowed and displayed motor racing at its finest.

Over 10 months and 16 races, the courage, skill, stamina and commitment of the major players still defies belief.

In one corner sat Niki Lauda, the seemingly metronomic Austrian driver, the 27-year-old World Champion in a Ferrari and a man for who winning seemed to be everything, and more.

He was pitted against James Hunt, a man who had scrapped his way to the top of Formula One and who the world loved as a debonair, headline-grabbing playboy.

While they seemed like polar opposites in terms of personalities, they both possessed the same nerve, talent, aggression, bravery and desire to win that would push them both to the very limit.

It would come down to one race, and one point, in a year full of controversies, brushes with mortality and moments of genius.

1976 was a truly unforgettable tussle that sealed James Hunt's spot in the pantheon of British sporting greats.

"I'M GOING TO GET LEGLESS"

- James Hunt, October 24, 1976

BRAZIL

RACE RESULT:

Pos	Name	Team	Time/Gap
1	Lauda	Ferrari	1:45:16.78
2	Depailler	Tyrell	+21.47
3	Pryce	Shadow	+23.84
4	Stuck	March	+1:28.17
5	Scheckter	Tyrell	+1:56:46
6	Mass	McLaren	+1:58.27

CHAMPIONSHIP TABLE

1	Lauda	9
2	Depailler	6
3	Pryce	4
4	Stuck	3

Hunt's opening Grand Prix weekend in a McLaren could not have got off to a better start.

It could not have finished worse, either.

With the eyes of the racing world watching Hunt and wondering how he would cope following his switch from Hesketh, he initially answered his critics well.

In addition to simply trying to get comfortable in his new car, the M23, Hunt also had to make it crystal clear to McLaren team-mate Jochen Mass that he was the No.1 driver.

A screaming and very public argument with team boss Teddy Mayer about how his car was set up more than did enough

to let everybody know that Hunt was not going to be pushed around and he backed up his words with actions, grabbing his first ever pole position by 200ths of a second from – who else? - Niki Lauda.

Hunt could not capitalise on his pole position, however.

Caught out by the new starting lights system, Hunt slipped into third after a slow start as Lauda and fellow Ferrari driver Clay Regazzoni sped past him.

It was a sign of what was to come.

Hunt got involved in a duel with Jean-Pierre Jarier, who seemed to endlessly pursue him around the Interlagos circuit, and although Hunt did more than enough to shake off his intentions, his McLaren then developed a fuel injection fault.

Hunt initially had no power and then too much of it as his throttle jammed open. He spun off the track, but the damage was done as the spin caused further damage that meant he had to retire.

"Hunt the Shunt" was, unfortunately, back in business, but this time it was by no means his fault.

Lauda eventually cruised home by a margin of more than 20 seconds – virtual light years in racing terms – as he picked up nine points to get his title defence off to the perfect start.

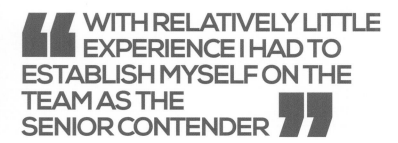

"WITH RELATIVELY LITTLE EXPERIENCE I HAD TO ESTABLISH MYSELF ON THE TEAM AS THE SENIOR CONTENDER"

SOUTH AFRICA

KYALAMI, MARCH 6, 1976

RACE RESULT:

Pos	Name	Team	Time/Gap
1	Lauda	Ferrari	1:42:18.4
2	Hunt	McLaren	+1.3
3	Mass	McLaren	+45.9
4	Scheckter	March	+1:08.4
5	Watson	Penske	+ 1 lap
6	Andretti	Parnelli	+ 1 lap

CHAMPIONSHIP TABLE

1	Lauda	18
2	Depailler	6
3	Hunt	6
4	Mass	5

Considering what was happening at home, this was one of Hunt's finest performances.

During the run-up to this Grand Prix it emerged that Suzy, tired of Hunt's unwillingness to take their marriage seriously, had begun a relationship with Hollywood icon Richard Burton.

It was the perfect tabloid story: the spurned sportsman, the beautiful blonde and the film star.

Journalists from around the world raced to Kyalami to try and get Hunt's reaction (which was remarkably sanguine – he actually agreed with Suzy's opinion of him as a terrible husband) and Hunt spent the days leading up to this race holed up in a private mansion many miles from the McLaren hotel, which was under siege from quote-hungry reporters.

Somehow, Hunt pushed his domestic situation to the back of his mind and again seized pole position with Lauda alongside him.

A sluggish start saw Lauda, Mass and Vittorio Brambilla overtake Hunt, but he soon fought back until only Lauda was in front of him.

Lauda originally had a 10-second lead, but a slow puncture meant Hunt was endlessly catching up.

However, the race ran out before the air in Lauda's tyre and he got over the line just ahead of Hunt by 1.3 seconds.

Nevertheless, Hunt was on the board.

> I STILL THINK NIKI CAN BE STOPPED. IT'S EARLY DAYS YET TO START DESPAIRING – EVEN THOUGH HE HAS A 12-POINT LEAD ALREADY AHEAD OF PATRICK AND MYSELF

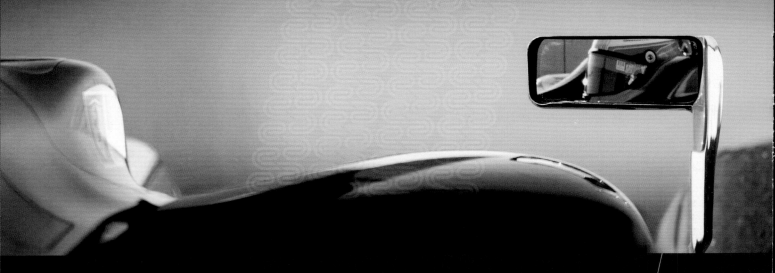

A service driven insurance broker for the fast moving world...

We offer the full spectrum of Motorsport insurance products in every major championship across the globe. On and off the track.

+44 (0)20 7444 6000
info@ellisclowes.com
ellisclowes.com

UNITED STATES

GRAND PRIX WEST, LONG BEACH, MARCH 28, 1976

RACE RESULT:

Pos	Name	Team	Time/Gap
1	Regazzoni	Ferrari	1:53:18.471
2	Lauda	Ferrari	+42.414
3	Depailler	Tyrell	+49.972
4	Laffite	Ligier	+1:12.828
5	Mass	McLaren	+1.22.292
6	Fittipaldi	Fittipaldi	+1 lap

CHAMPIONSHIP TABLE

1	Lauda	24
2	Depailler	10
3	Regazzoni	9
4	Mass	7

The inaugural US Grand Prix West, in the salubrious surroundings of Long Beach, California, saw an almighty contest that confirmed Lauda's Formula One World Championship defence was going better than he could have ever hoped.

Although it was Lauda's Ferrari team-mate Regazzoni who picked up the victory, Lauda's second-place finish happily increased his World Championship tally and gave him a 14-point advantage over French driver Patrick Depailler.

If Hunt was upset enough about seeing Lauda back on the podium, that was nothing compared to his feelings towards Depailler, who had caused his premature exit from the race.

On lap four, Hunt saw a gap and tried to slip inside Depailler, but the Tyrell driver saw him coming and closed the opportunity. They continued to tussle until they left the corner side-by-side, at which point Depailler pushed Hunt closer to the barriers – which Hunt eventually hit.

This caused Hunt's volcanic temper to the surface as he stormed from the car and gesticulated at Depailler every time he sped past in his unblemished car.

Hunt's afternoon in the Californian sun had been a disaster and he was falling ever further behind those hoping to end Lauda's Formula One dominance.

SPAIN

CIRCUITO DEL JARAMA, MAY 2, 1976

In a nutshell, Hunt was in pole position, Hunt won the race and Hunt was delighted.

But not for long.

This Grand Prix saw the unique six-wheeler Formula One car make its debut. Driven by Depailler, the Tyrell car broke no rules as regulations against six-wheeled cars had never been written. However, the innovation of that car – and its legality – would eventually be overshadowed by other car design issues that ruined McLaren – and Hunt's – weekend.

In this race, Hunt benefited from a freak injury to Lauda, who had broken two ribs in the lead-up to the race when he was involved in a tractor accident. The Austrian said he could still feel them grinding together and he wore strapping to try and keep them from moving.

It would not be the last time Lauda's phenomenal courage was displayed in the 1976 season.

Lauda took an early lead but the pain from his midsection was simply too much to bear towards the middle part of the race. Hunt overtook him on lap 32 and remained in front until the end while Lauda gritted his teeth and took second place.

> ## THE PUNISHMENT TOTALLY FAILS TO FIT THE CRIME AND WE SHALL BE APPEALING ALL THE WAY. ONE THING IS FOR SURE – IT'S NICE TO WIN AND I'M AT MY MOST DANGEROUS WHEN RILED

Yet, just as McLaren began to pour the champagne, they received bad news.

F1 bosses had measured their car across the back wheels and found that it was just 1.8cm too wide, prompting a sensational disqualification for Hunt.

Hunt's Goodyear tyres had expanded too much in the heat and pushed the car outside the allowed boundaries

Furious arguments went back and forth but to little use as Hunt was disqualified and Lauda given the nine World Championship points. McLaren appealed and had their hands full in the months to come.

Meanwhile, Lauda moved into a 23-point lead and the season looked over before it had barely started.

BOTTOM LEFT: Hunt driving a supreme race in Spain
ABOVE: A Mirror report on the post-race fallout
OPPOSITE PAGE: Hunt on the podium with King Juan Carlos

RACE RESULT:

Pos	Name	Team	Time/Gap
1	Hunt	McLaren	1:42:20.43
2	Lauda	Ferrari	30.97
3	Nilsson	Lotus	48.02
4	Reutemann	Brabham	+ 1 lap
5	Amon	Ensign	+ 1 lap
6	Pace	Brabham	+ 1 lap

CHAMPIONSHIP TABLE

1	Lauda	33
2	Depailler	10
3	Regazzoni	9
4	Mass	7

BELGIUM

Lauda's World Championship lead was looking insurmountable.

The Austrian grabbed pole position with Regazzoni in second and Hunt in third. Although the legal niceties had meant Hunt was denied the points in Spain, his confidence following an impressive drive was still high and he had hopes of "winning" back-to-back races to try and get some form of foothold, no matter how small, in the race to catch Lauda.

No such luck.

Although Lauda's ribs were still hurting – this race was just a fortnight after he struggled his way around the Spanish Grand Prix – he never really looked in trouble.

Hunt briefly threatened him as he moved up from third on the grid to second at the start, but Regazzoni raced intelligently and Hunt quickly dropped back to sixth.

It was a bad day at the office for McLaren. With power and control lacking, Hunt wrestled with his car but could not make any inroads and, in the end, transmission trouble brought his afternoon's work to a premature end.

Lauda went on to win from Ferrari team-mate Regazzoni as his procession of a season continued unabated.

It was getting to the stage where even Hunt had given up. Lauda's lead was 36 points over him and with an inconsistent car, plus the legal issues surrounding the Spanish result overshadowing the season, Hunt and McLaren headed to Monaco with heavy hearts.

RACE RESULT:

Pos	Name	Team	Time/Gap
1	Lauda	Ferrari	1:42:53.23
2	Regazzoni	Ferrari	3.46
3	Laffite	Ligier	35.38
4	Scheckter	Tyrell	1:31.00
5	Jones	Surtees	+1 lap
6	Mass	McLaren	+1 lap

CHAMPIONSHIP TABLE

1	Lauda	42
2	Regazzoni	15
3	Depailler	10
4	Mass	8

MONACO

MONACO, MAY 30, 1976

RACE RESULT:

Pos	Name	Team	Time/Gap
1	Lauda	Ferrari	1:59:51.47
2	Scheckter	Tyrell	+11.13
3	Depailler	Tyrell	+1:04.84
4	Stuck	March	+ 1 lap
5	Mass	McLaren	+ 1 lap
6	Fittipaldi	Fittipaldi	+ 1 lap

CHAMPIONSHIP TABLE

1	Lauda	51
2	Regazzoni	15
3	Depailler	14
4	Scheckter	14

Different race, same outcome.

The dominance of Ferrari, whether that be Lauda or Regazzoni, continued in Monaco as the duo were first and second on the grid respectively, while Lauda picked up yet another victory.

Hunt had a shocking weekend - from start to finish.

The handling and transmission problems that had cursed his M23 in recent months could not be shaken off. The car was unresponsive, would oversteer heavily and Hunt's confidence in his own safety was at an all-time low. Hunt, like every Formula One driver, was a brave man, but even he must have had his doubts about his chances of coming through races unscathed in a car that was causing constant headaches for him and the McLaren mechanics.

A terrible qualifying session saw him start the Monaco race in 14th spot on the grid - almost instantly wiping out any chances of success - and so it proved.

During the race, Hunt battled nobly but his engine eventually blew up, causing his retirement.

Hunt was still stranded on six points with Lauda well into the distance on 51. Hunt was now so far behind that the world title was just a pipe dream. If anything, his biggest challenge between now and the end of the season would be to convince McLaren that he was still their No.1 driver.

Although Mass was also well behind Lauda, he came fifth in Monaco to give him 10 points for the season, four more than McLaren's "leading" man.

From his car to team politics to the World Championship table, everywhere Hunt looked, he found big problems.

SWEDEN

SCANDINAVIAN RACEWAY, JUNE 13, 1976

RACE RESULT:

Pos	Name	Team	Time/Gap
1	Scheckter	Tyrell	1:46:53.729
2	Depailler	Tyrell	+19.766
3	Lauda	Ferrari	+33.866
4	Laffite	Ligier	+55.819
5	Hunt	McLaren	+59.819
6	Regazzoni	Ferrari	+1:00.366

CHAMPIONSHIP TABLE

1	Lauda	55
2	Scheckter	23
3	Depailler	20
4	Regazzoni	16

This was more like it.

Although Hunt only managed to pick up two points at the Swedish Grand Prix, courtesy of finishing in fifth place, it at least showed that McLaren and Hunt had started to get to the bottom of their unco-operative car.

Hunt had terrible practice and qualifying sessions, his car acting more like a bucking bronco than a racing vehicle, and it soon became clear in the race that a podium finish was unlikely.

However, he stuck it out and drove as hard as he dared.

At the front, Jody Scheckter and Depailler got to work in silencing those critics who had poured scorn on their six-wheeled cars, finishing in first and second place respectively.

It was the first time in the season that Lauda had not been in the top two, which gave Hunt some heart. However, the Austrian still picked up four points, meaning his lead extended further still.

Scheckter was his closest title rival, 32 points behind, while Hunt could barely be seen in Lauda's wing mirrors, an incredible 47 points off top position. For Hunt, the season looked as good as over.

> ALTHOUGH WE WERE NEVER IN WITH CHANCE OF WINNING, WE WERE REALLY QUITE SATISFIED WITH THE RESULT AND IT FELT GOOD TO BE IN THE POINTS AGAIN AFTER SUCH A LONG TIME. I ENJOYED MY WEEKEND IN SWEDEN...

FRANCE

Or maybe not.

Before this race, Lauda had more than twice as many points as his nearest rival Scheckter, never mind Hunt.

After starting on pole, with Lauda next to him on the starting grid, Hunt knew he had to finish in front of the Austrian if he was to have any chance whatsoever of pulling off a motoring miracle.

Lauda had a cracking start, flying past Hunt to take the lead from his English rival.

But Hunt's luck was in.

On the ninth lap, just as Lauda seemed to be settling in for the long haul – and another nine points – his Ferrari engine fell to pieces.

Regazzoni came chasing after Hunt as Ferrari looked to reimpose themselves on the race, but he also suffered engine failure and had to retire, allowing Hunt to claim his second dramatic win of the season and third of his career.

Hunt had enjoyed a great weekend in France, and this was an indication that he wasn't about to give up on the World Championship any time soon.

RACE RESULT:

Pos	Name	Team	Time/Gap
1	Hunt	McLaren	1:40:58.60
2	Depailler	Tyrell	+12.70
3	Watson	Penske	+23.55
4	Pace	Brabham	+24.82
5	Andretti	Lotus	+43.92
6	Scheckter	Tyrell	+55.07

CHAMPIONSHIP TABLE

1	Lauda	55
2	Depailler	26
3	Scheckter	24
4	Hunt	17

A BRITISH HERO

If there is anything better than winning one Grand Prix, surely it is winning two Grands Prix in two days?

Straight after Hunt's France success, he went to Paris to see how McLaren's appeal had gone following the Spanish Grand Prix disqualification earlier in the season for having a car that was millimetres too wide.

A panel of Formula One experts heard legal representations from all sides before, finally, the bubbly could be opened for the second time in 24 hours.

Rather than face disqualification, McLaren had to pay a fine and Hunt was reinstated as the race winner, regaining nine points.

All of a sudden, he had picked up 18 World Championship points in no time at all and, just as importantly, the downgrading of Lauda from winner to second place meant the Austrian lost three points himself.

Hunt was now up to 26 for the season, which gave him a glimmer of hope – but a win at Brands Hatch, his home Grand Prix, was now crucial if he was to close the gap on Lauda any further.

"All I could do was keep winning," Hunt said. "There was still no real pressure on me."

Brands Hatch saw yet another extraordinary race; a contest full of yet more legal scrutiny, more raised voices and more drama than anybody could have imagined.

Hunt started second on the grid, but his afternoon looked over before it had barely begun.

Just seconds after the start, Lauda and Regazzoni collided – Regazzoni generally being blamed for the accident – and Hunt's McLaren got caught up in the melee. Hunt was actually airborne for a short while and gravity did him few favours when he landed as it soon became clear that his car was damaged and his race was in doubt.

This is when events really became interesting.

Red flags were flown around Brands Hatch to indicate that the race would have to be stopped on safety grounds as there was too much debris on the track.

This gave Hunt half a chance of continuing in the McLaren spare car, or so he thought.

In chaotic scenes, Hunt jumped from his stricken vehicle – complete with a damaged thumb – and raced back to the pits to use the spare McLaren.

Or maybe not.

After intense discussions, Formula One officials decided that they would only allow spare cars for all drivers who had completed the original, red-flagged first lap.

But Hunt had not completed it.

Despite the fact he was still moving when the red flags were shown now meant nothing as he had then pulled over to one side. That was used as evidence that his car had been too badly damaged to continue, therefore making the spare car illegal.

And it looked like this legal footnote would be ending Hunt's British Grand Prix and with it his World Championship hopes.

When the British crowd were told that their hero was being denied the opportunity to race at his home Grand Prix, the booing and jeering for the men in blazers was deafening.

Before long, furious arguments were taking place as McLaren team manager

Alastair Caldwell got involved in debating the ruling.

In the meantime, the McLaren team were playing a blinder.

As Caldwell argued McLaren's case, the guys in the garage used this time to good effect, working on Hunt's original car in a bid to get it back into a race-worthy condition.

Caldwell bought the McLaren mechanics enough time to produce a miracle, sorting out Hunt's damaged suspension, and it was driven back out ▶

BRANDS HATCH, JULY 18, 1976

onto the track, good to go.

Eventually, race officials – mindful of the restless crowd and the fact almost an hour had now passed – relented and allowed Hunt back into the race.

"Hunt ran past and I tried to grab a quick word with him," Murray Walker, working as a pit lane reporter on the day, recalls. "He stopped, looked at me and said, 'There is a race on, dear old boy, there is still a race on.' And there was."

In months to come, this would be the subject of yet more legal debate and protests as Ferrari appealed the decision.

But before that, there was a race to be won.

When the impatient fans finally got to see some action, they were not let down.

Both Hunt and Lauda – fired up and ready for another duel – broke the fastest lap record as Hunt chased down the Austrian. His hastily repaired car somehow got easier to drive as the race continued and on lap 45 Hunt pounced, passing Lauda and going on to win.

The British crowd understandably went wild and, although speculation about the legality of Hunt's win would rumble on for months, for now he was well and truly back in action.

"There was no way I was going to miss that race," he said. "The organisers had decided that even if I might later be disqualified, they were going to start me. I had a long struggle to get past Lauda – I was always going to be a lot quicker once I had."

The next stop was Germany and the formidable Nurburgring. More headlines were to follow, although this time they would be more dreadful than dramatic.

RACE RESULT:

Pos	Name	Team	Time/Gap
1	Hunt	McLaren	1:43:27:61
2	Lauder	Ferrari	+52.95
3	Scheckter	Tyrell	+1:07.13
4	Watson	Penske	+ 1 lap
5	Pryce	Shadow-Ford	+ 1 lap
6	Fittipaldi	Fittipaldi	+ 2 laps

CHAMPIONSHIP TABLE

1	Lauda	58
2	Hunt	35
3	Scheckter	28
4	Depailler	26

" IT WAS CERTAINLY MY MOST EMOTIONAL RACE. YOU FEEL THE CROWD MORE THAN YOU DO ANYWHERE ELSE AND FROM THE CROWD'S POINT OF VIEW I HAD THE PERFECT RACE "

One moment James would be sat in a stifling hot cockpit, racing on the brink, the next he would be sat at the backgammon board, fixated by the game. At both, he wanted to desperately win

GERMANY

RACE RESULT:

Pos	Name	Team	Time/Gap
1	Hunt	McLaren	1:41:42:7
2	Scheckter	Tyrell	+27.7
3	Mass	McLaren	+52.4
4	Pace	Brabham	+54.2
5	Nilsson	Lotus	+1:57:3
6	Stommelen	Brabham	+2:30:3

CHAMPIONSHIP TABLE

1	Lauda	58
2	Hunt	44
3	Scheckter	34
4	Depailler	26

In normal circumstances, Hunt winning the German Grand Prix would have been cause for wild celebrations.

The comeback was on - that was all that mattered, surely?

In fact, neither Hunt nor anybody else at the Nurburgring that August day gave the result of this race much thought at all. The only images flashing through their minds - and through the minds of the watching world - were the scenes of fiery carnage caused by a horrendous incident involving Lauda.

In another world, on another day, Lauda would have died on the tarmac in Germany, such was the ferocity of the crash and subsequent fireball that changed his life.

The Nurburgring is not nicknamed "The Green Hell" for nothing.

Based in the Eifel mountains, a lap was more than 14 miles long, encompassed 150-plus corners and had claimed the lives of scores of drivers.

It was a brooding, lethal racetrack with changing weather conditions, treacherous corners and virtually no protection.

If you crashed badly at the Nurburgring, you usually died. It was as simple and as brutally black and white as that.

Before this race, Lauda led a personal charge to have the race boycotted. It was simply too dangerous and all drivers too brave for their own good.

However, under threatening black clouds, the race went ahead.

On just the second lap, it became clear that something had gone wrong somewhere as Lauda's car was taking an age to pass the pit-lane.

And that's because it was ablaze at the far end of the circuit.

Lauda's car left the track and he collided heavily with the ruthless barriers.

Instantly alight, the car ricocheted back into the middle of the track where it was then hit by Brett Lunger and Harald Ertl, both men simply horrified and helpless as

> **" I AM DESPERATELY SORRY THAT IT WAS CLOUDED BY NIKI'S ACCIDENT AND THAT IT LOOKS AS IF THE WORLD CHAMPIONSHIP WILL BE DECIDED WITH NIKI AWAY FROM THE TRACK "**

" I WANTED NIKI TO BE WELL AND RACING AGAIN – I DIDN'T WANT TO BEAT HIM WHILE HE WAS LYING IN A HOSPITAL BED "

their cars did not have time to miss Lauda's inferno.

Lauda was sat in his cockpit, conscious and terrified, as his helmet had come off and he was burning to death. There really is no other way of describing it. Lauda was dying, right there, in the middle of the Nurburgring.

Eventually, Lunger, Ertl, Guy Edwards and Arturo Merzario managed to beat back the roaring flames long enough to help get Lauda out and, initially, the dazed Austrian was able to walk away from the incident, albeit it with his head and scalp already very badly damaged.

It was to get worse.

Lauda's condition soon deteriorated as his scorched lungs and third-degree burns nearly took his life. He was even given the Last Rites, such was the scale of his injuries.

Before that, though, there was still a race to be won and Hunt was determined to seize his chance. At the time, he had no idea how badly hurt Lauda was and, if he did, perhaps he would have had grave concerns about going back out onto a racetrack that was clearly extremely, insanely, dangerous.

Hunt was in superb form after the

restart and led from the beginning, leaving Scheckter and Mass to fight it out for the other podium finishes.

The gap between Lauda and Hunt had again drastically shortened. Yet, with Lauda lying in a hospital bed with a heavily bandaged scalp and face – and with lungs struggling to function – all thoughts lay with the Austrian rather than the Englishman.

Hunt was as touched and as concerned about Niki as anybody but also thought that Lauda's season – perhaps even his career – was over.

How wrong he was.

AUSTRIA

ÖSTERREICHRING, AUGUST 15, 1976

RACE RESULT:

Pos	Name	Team	Time/Gap
1	Watson	Penske	1:30:07.86
2	Laffite	Ligier	+10.79
3	Nilsson	Lotus	+11.98
4	Hunt	McLaren	+12.44
5	Andretti	Lotus	+ 21.49
6	Peterson	March	+ 34.34

CHAMPIONSHIP TABLE

1	Lauda	58
2	Hunt	47
3	Scheckter	34
4	Depailler	26

While Lauda fought for his life, the season rolled on to Austria, but there's no doubt that events were overshadowed by Lauda's incident.

However, remarkably enough, just a fortnight after he nearly died, Lauda was already well enough to watch this race on the television.

To use the word "miraculous" might be stretching the case, but there is no doubt that his recovery totally and utterly confounded the medical profession.

There had been calls beforehand for the Austrian Grand Prix to be abandoned due to Lauda's injuries and Ferrari did not take part in the race as a protest against what they perceived as an injustice: Hunt both regaining his Spanish Grand Prix points as well as being allowed to race at Brands Hatch.

As a result of Ferrari's absence, this race had little glitz or glamour, but Northern Ireland's John Watson held off Jacques Laffite to claim his first Grand Prix victory.

It was simply an off day for Hunt but, crucially, he did still manage to pick up fourth place and the three points that came with it.

A car that never felt truly balanced all

weekend hindered Hunt's chances in Austria, but he did what he could in the circumstances he was given. In a way, it was a superbly professional performance.

He knew a win was unlikely so did all he could to wrestle an unwieldy car around the 54 laps of the Österreichring and took a lot of confidence from the result. Hunt was still ticking over nicely.

> **I SPOKE TO NIKI AFTER THE RACE AND I CAN CONFIRM THAT HE'S LOST NONE OF HIS CHARM AND GOOD HUMOUR BECAUSE HE WASTED NO TIME IN TELLING ME HOW DELIGHTED HE WAS THAT I HADN'T WON**

HOLLAND

RACE RESULT:

Pos	Name	Team	Time/Gap
1	Hunt	McLaren	1:44:52.09
2	Regazzoni	Ferrari	+0.92
3	Andretti	Lotus	+2.09
4	Pryce	Shadow	+6.94
5	Scheckter	Tyrell	+22.46
6	Brambilla	March	+45.03

CHAMPIONSHIP TABLE

1	Lauda	58
2	Hunt	56
3	Scheckter	36
4	Depailler	26

Hunt needed history to repeat itself if he wanted to keep up the pressure on the still stricken Lauda.

A year earlier, the Englishman's career had really exploded into life at this circuit, holding off the Austrian for what seemed like forever to record his first Grand Prix victory.

And now, on his 29th birthday, he would once again taste victory - an utterly crucial one that cut the gap even further between himself and his major rival.

Ronnie Peterson started on pole position with Hunt next to him and an almighty tussle began that become one of the season's major talking points.

Hunt, by his own admission, never had to work harder to stand atop the podium.

Firstly, he had to chase down Peterson, who made an excellent start while Watson - fresh on the back of his win in Austria - was also a thorn in Hunt's side.

Eventually, Hunt capitalised on a Watson error to move into second place before Hunt then wrestled the lead from Peterson.

Watson would not be thrown off Hunt's scent, though, and the two of them slugged it out for the next 70 minutes before Watson had mechanical trouble and had to retire.

Hunt was also wrestling with his car - but despite intense late competition from Regazzoni, who was doing his best to get Ferrari back in front of McLaren, Hunt held on to win by a drastically small margin.

No matter, nine points is nine points - and Hunt was now well on the charge.

> **IT WAS PROBABLY THE HARDEST RACE I'VE EVER DRIVEN IN TERMS OF SHEER PHYSICAL HARD WORK AND THERE WAS A GOOD DEAL OF PRESSURE ON ME TO DO WELL**

WIN JAMES HUNT MEMORABILIA!

Texaco® Havoline®, sponsors of James Hunt during his historic 1976 Formula One™ World Championship winning season, are offering F1 fans the opportunity to win exclusive James Hunt memorabilia, in partnership with the James Hunt Estate. **Prizes include:**

- James Hunt Goodie Bag – *including JH weekend bag, JH wash bag, JH mini helmet, JH Belstaff t-shirt, JH magazine*
- JH Helmet – *full size JH replica helmet signed by Tom and Freddie Hunt*
- 5x mini JH replica helmets signed by Tom and Freddie Hunt
- 4x JH Limited Edition framed prints signed by artist Jeremy Houghton
- Silverstone Classic VIP hospitality tickets – *including meeting Freddie Hunt, hotel, transfers, £250 spending money*
- Silverstone Classic General Admission tickets

Be first off the grid! Visit **www.jameshunt76.com** to enter for FREE…and join in the 40 year celebrations

There are three competitions, starting 27 June 2016.
Visit the site for more details and competition rules.

www.jameshunt76.com /JamesHuntFoundation

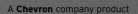

RACE RESULT:

Pos	Name	Team	Time/Gap
1	Peterson	March	1:30:35.6
2	Regazzoni	Ferrari	+2.3
3	Laffite	Ligier	+3.0
4	Lauda	Ferrari	+19.4
5	Scheckter	Tyrell	+19.5
6	Depailler	March	+35.7

CHAMPIONSHIP TABLE

1	Lauda	61
2	Hunt	56
3	Scheckter	38
4	Regazzoni	28

> " NIKI'S RECOVERY AND FIGHTING DRIVE WAS ALMOST UNBELIEVABLE AND HAVING HAD A LONG, LONG CONVERSATION WITH HIM BEFORE THE RACE I WAS CONVINCED THAT HE WAS AS FIT TO RACE AS HE HAS EVER BEEN "

Across the entire spectrum of sporting achievements and endeavour - no matter the discipline, decade or century - few moments can capture the imagination as much as this Grand Prix.

Little over a month earlier, Niki Lauda had been given up for dead and yet here he was, back in the very sport that had so nearly killed him.

Lauda's helmet had to be widened to allow him to fit it over the bandages that still swathed his scalp and his head regularly bled during qualification and the race itself.

It was a superlative display of courage, determination, mental strength and tenacity - and nobody was as impressed as Hunt.

However, Lauda's return in a Ferrari - in the home nation of Ferrari as well, don't forget - could not be truly enjoyed by Hunt due to yet more trouble with the authorities.

After qualifying on the Saturday, his fuel was deemed to be illegal by inspection chiefs as it allegedly contained too much octane.

That saw him relegated to the back of the grid for the race, much to the delight of the baying Italian crowd.

Hunt had nothing to lose and went all out to work his way through the field. However, despite making good progress, his bad fortune continued as he and Tom Pryce came together and Hunt was out.

His walk back to the pit lane did nothing to further his mood as the Italian public let him know exactly what they thought of him.

Meanwhile, Lauda - battling near-crippling nerves and fear - showed superhuman bravery to finish fourth. The three points he picked up gave him a five-point lead over Hunt.

It was still anyone's for the taking.

But Hunt was about to face another legal blow that threatened to tear the entire season apart.

RACE RESULT:

Pos	Name	Team	Time/Gap
1	Hunt	McLaren	1:40:09.626
2	Depailler	Tyrell	+6.331
3	Andretti	Lotus	+10.366
4	Scheckter	Tyrell	+19.745
5	Mass	McLaren	+41.811
6	Regazzoni	Ferrari	+46.256

CHAMPIONSHIP TABLE

1	Lauda	64
2	Hunt	56
3	Scheckter	43
4	Depailler	33

> **THAT WAS PROBABLY THE TOUGHEST RACE I HAVE EVER WON. PATRICK WAS PUSHING ME HARDER THAN I WANTED TO BE PUSHED. IT WAS CLIFFHANGING STUFF, TOO CLIFFHANGING FOR ME. WE WERE ON THE LIMIT ALL THE WAY**

Before this race, Hunt received some devastating news.

Ferrari's protests about the legality of his Brands Hatch win back in July were upheld – courtesy of Lauda himself showing up at the hearing to back up his team's argument – and the British driver was disqualified from that race.

The absurdity of somebody being stripped of Grand Prix points months after the event was not lost on McLaren or Hunt and he furiously railed against the decision, but to no avail.

The ruling meant Lauda now had 64 points with Hunt, left scoreless by the decision, back on 47.

It also meant the end of the season looked like fizzling out as Hunt now appeared to be too far behind to catch the Austrian.

If Hunt was to stand any chance, however miniscule, then he had to win in Canada.

His spirits were understandably low as McLaren landed in Toronto and he seemed past the point of caring, getting spectacularly drunk in the nights before the race as he felt his season was over.

Or was it?

In another extraordinary twist – and an extraordinary race – Hunt put his M23, and his booze-riddled body, through the paces at Mosport Park, claiming a brilliant pole position.

He then drove right on the edge – after all, what did he now have to lose? – and dominated the race from start to finish in a ride that was perhaps his most impressive ever, if only because of how much beer he had consumed in the previous 36 hours.

Lauda, on the other hand, was crippled by mechanical problems and could only manage eighth place. That brought him zero points whereas Hunt picked up the customary nine, which lessened the damage caused by his Brands Hatch disappointment.

The door to the World Championship was still ajar. Just.

USA

Hunt and Lauda both knew that this Grand Prix could decide who won the title that season.

With Hunt having closed the gap on his main rival, and with them back on friendly terms after a frosty few days following the Brands Hatch decision, Hunt got his weekend off to a flier with his eighth pole position of the season.

Yet in a repeat of a quirk that bothered Hunt all season, he was beaten out of the blocks by Scheckter, whose impressive season under the radar continued in the USA.

A fascinating race began to develop. Scheckter set the pace in first with Hunt safely in behind him while Lauda sat in third place.

Each man waited their moment to try and pounce. A wrong move from Hunt at any time would have probably signalled the end of his season. 'Hunt the Shunt' simply could not afford to appear.

If anything marks the evolution of Hunt into a really talented Formula One driver it was perhaps this race as he wrestled with an oversteering car and also the pressure he was under. In other words, he had to race for his life, mixing courage with craft to get every ounce of power he could from the McLaren.

By lap 36, Hunt seized his moment and overtook Scheckter, but the South African soon regained the lead as Hunt struggled to overtake a straggling car at the back of the field.

Hunt – rather than the hair-trigger young man of old – kept calm and worked his way back into contention behind Scheckter.

Finally, Hunt got another chance to pass and seized it, speeding through on a corner that looks eye-wateringly dangerous on television, never mind from the cockpit.

Hunt was in front. He held on and with Scheckter coming in second and Lauda in third, the gap in the World Championship table was cut to three points.

Japan awaited with Hunt knowing exactly what he had to do, which was come at least third and hope for dear life that Lauda – the "bravest man he knew" – would not be ahead of him.

The most breathtaking finish in the most breathtaking of seasons had been perfectly set up.

RACE RESULT:

Pos	Name	Team	Time/Gap
1	Hunt	McLaren	1:42:40.742
2	Scheckter	Tyrell	+8.030
3	Lauda	Ferrari	+1:02.324
4	Mass	McLaren	+1:02.458
5	Stuck	March	+1:07.978
6	Watson	Penske	+1:08.190

CHAMPIONSHIP TABLE

1	Lauda	68
2	Hunt	65
3	Scheckter	49
4	Depailler	33

As the rain fell in torrents in Japan, a legend was made. To race in this weather was crazy, suicidal, reckless – and astonishingly brave.

The rain-drenched Fuji track resembled a lake, water pouring down and across it from all directions while mist descended and wind battered the track.

Apart from the race leader, every driver knew they would spend the afternoon peering into a wall of water, driving on instinct, luck and boldness.

From the safe viewpoint of four decades, the fact it was allowed to go ahead in the first place seems criminally negligent.

Clearly, Formula One had learned nothing from Lauda's brush

with death.

For Lauda to even contemplate getting into his vehicle in those conditions is a further testament to his extraordinary courage.

Both Lauda and Hunt wanted to postpone the race. Hunt had always had a strong sense of how closely he was living to the edge while Lauda only needed to take one look in the mirror to see just how perilous a job he had.

"Niki and I were both on the safety committee," Hunt said.

"We were both against racing that day because of the conditions. We thought it should have been held over until the next day. The track was flooded."

JAPAN

FUJI SPEEDWAY, OCTOBER 24, 1976

"IT'S BEEN A LONG, TIRING AND INCREDIBLY EXCITING SEASON FOR ALL OF US. BUT FOR ME THERE WAS ONE CLOUD HANGING OVER IT. THAT WAS NIKI'S NURBURGRING ACCIDENT AND IF THERE IS ANYTHING I WOULD LIKE TO HAVE CHANGED IT WOULD HAVE BEEN TO HAVE RACED HIM TO THE TITLE IN EVERY SINGLE ROUND"

However, despite their best attempts, neither driver could convince the rest of the field that they should hold off until the weather improved, so both men literally took their life in their hands for a final time that season.

Ironically enough, despite his very real fears about his imminent health and safety, Hunt had perhaps his best start of the season – if not his career.

He launched his car into the lead through the horrendous puddles that covered the track and that at least meant his view was unimpeded.

He had had the dream start – and it was about to get better.

After just two laps, Lauda returned to the pits and his race was over.

Was it engine trouble, suspension issues or tyre problems?

It was none of these. Lauda had decided to come into the pits, jump out of his car and walk away with his life.

Those opening two laps, driving virtually blind, had told him that the risks being taken were too crazy to endure and too dangerous to be justified.

The Austrian was to go on and win two more World Championships, yet his most admirable, courageous moment remains that decision to pull into the pits in Japan.

There are more important things in life than winning, such as life itself, and Lauda had more than earned the right to decide when a race was too dangerous to continue.

His retirement changed the landscape entirely, meaning Hunt now only needed to come third to win the title.

Yet, if Lauda's decision to stop had been dramatic enough, it was nothing compared to the events about to unfold.

Brambilla took up the chance to chase down Hunt but span out on the 22nd lap, while Mass did the same shortly afterwards.

It seemed as if everything was going in Hunt's favour until the weather took a turn for the better, or for the worse, depending on your viewpoint.

The Fuji track began to dry out significantly. That started to wear out Hunt's wet-specific tyres and, although some of the field started to purposely seek out the ever-shrinking puddles in order to cool their tyres down, Hunt

JAPAN

FUJI SPEEDWAY, OCTOBER 24, 1976

persisted in trying to take the fastest racing line.

Eventually, this started to cost Hunt as Depailler and then Mario Andretti overtook him, meaning his margin for error was now zero.

On and on Hunt drove in his unsuitable tyres, shredding them and leaving chunks of rubber all over the Japanese track.

A lack of communication then followed between him and the McLaren pit.

Caldwell and Mayer became increasingly frantic as they wanted him to come in and a stand-off followed as Hunt stayed out far too long on his rapidly weakening tyres.

Finally, Hunt had to go in for a lengthy pit stop as his front left tyre lay on the verge of falling off completely. By the time he had slicks on, he had no idea what position he was in or what he had to do to get his precious third place.

"The front tyre started shredding, I had rubbish all over my visor and I didn't ⊙

JAPAN

know what the hell to do," Hunt recalled. "Then the tyre burst. I dropped some places during the pit stop, but I didn't know how many."

Despite widespread confusion about what position he was in – was he third? Fourth? Sixth? – the British driver knew he only had five laps left to rescue the position.

Blocking out the anger he felt at the miscommunication with the McLaren team, Hunt vowed simply to drive.

Drive, drive, drive.

Drive faster and harder than he had ever driven before.

All the years of early struggle; of ditching his car in Oulton Park lake; of fighting and fending for himself in Formula Ford; of dragging himself into the spotlight with Hesketh; of earning his McLaren stripes and clawing his way back into contention against the wonderful Lauda – everything came down to his performance in the closing laps.

It started to work. He edged past Regazzoni and Alan Jones until in front of him lay only Depailler and Andretti. The chequered flag came and went in a misty blur. Hunt had his third place and his long-awaited title.

Yet, he did not even realise.

As he continued his path around the Fuji track after crossing the finishing line, an irate Hunt was still clueless about where he had finished.

"I wasn't absolutely sure that I'd made it until I got back to the pits," Hunt said.

"If I hadn't been for my helmet, I would have bitten my nails all the way round the slowing-down lap."

Hunt parked his vehicle and stormed out of the cockpit, ready to punch the first McLaren team member he came across, such was his fury at the tyre mix-up and his lost moment of glory.

But all's well that ends well.

Teddy Mayer managed to calm Hunt enough and kept holding three fingers up. You've come third James. You've done enough. You've beaten Niki.

Finally, he could believe.

Finally, James Simon Wallis Hunt was the 1976 Formula One World Champion.

RACE RESULT:

Pos	Name	Team	Time/Gap
1	Andretti	Lotus	1:43:58.86
2	Depailler	Tyrell	+ 1 lap
3	Hunt	McLaren	+ 1 lap
4	Jones	Surtees	+ 1 lap
5	Regazzoni	Ferrari	+ 1 lap
6	Nilsson	Lotus	+ 1 lap

CHAMPIONSHIP TABLE

1	Hunt	69
2	Lauda	68
3	Scheckter	49
4	Depailler	39

FRIENDS
AND OCCASIONAL
FOES

James Hunt and Niki Lauda threw everything they had at each other during their careers, but on a personal level their relationship was the perfect example of grace under fire – and friendship in the most exceptional of circumstances...

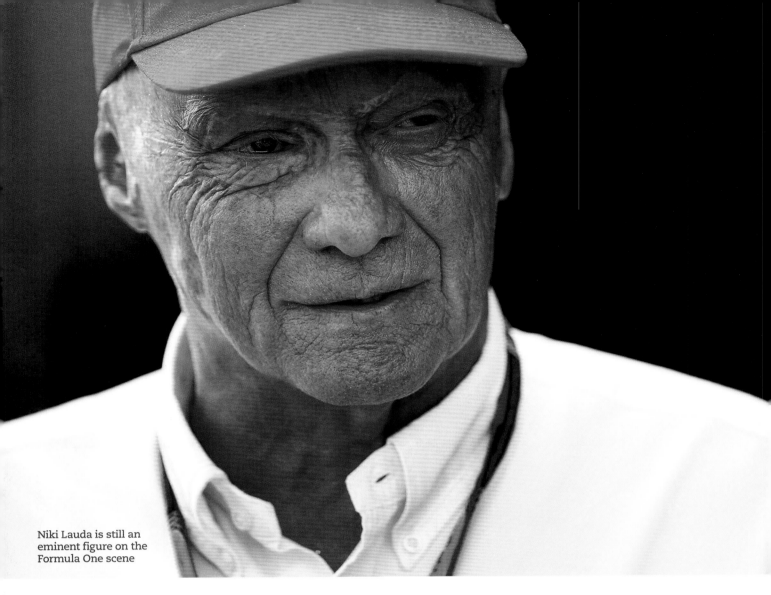

Niki Lauda is still an eminent figure on the Formula One scene

One was a quiet but intense and straight-talking Austrian, totally and utterly fixated with winning Grands Prix and the World Championship.

The other was a tall, glamorous playboy as popular with his fellow racers as he was the general public and media, a guy happy in the glare of the spotlight.

On paper, the two had very little in common - apart from a thirst for podium finishes.

Yet, Niki Lauda and James Hunt shared a level of friendship and respect that defied all logic and odds.

In 1976, with everything at stake, Hunt and Lauda still managed to remain friendly - particularly after Lauda's horrendous crash.

The Austrian's comeback just weeks after avoiding death stunned the sporting world and drew widespread admiration from Hunt himself.

"After the accident, it seemed as if all I would have to do was finish the last few races to win the Championship," Hunt said.

"What nobody knew was that Niki was making the most unbelievable recovery and was determined to come back so he could retain his title.

"Let nobody say Niki's retirement in Japan was the action of a coward or someone who has lost his nerve. Niki Lauda is the bravest man I've ever known and I mean it when I say that I would have been happier had we been able to share the Championship."

Hunt always defended Lauda's personality and the way he could often be brutally honest with other drivers and Formula One officials.

Nobody would have been surprised if

" NIKI LAUDA IS THE BRAVEST MAN I'VE EVER KNOWN AND I MEAN IT WHEN I SAY THAT I WOULD HAVE BEEN HAPPIER HAD WE BEEN ABLE TO SHARE THE CHAMPIONSHIP "

the tensions that the 1976 season contained – especially between the often feuding Ferrari and McLaren teams – had filtered down to the men sat in behind their respective steering wheels.

Yet, Hunt and Lauda ignored all the extra noise and, although the public perception might have been that there was little love lost between the two, Hunt never stopped praising his closest rival.

"I don't have many close friends in the motor-racing world," he said. "Unlike tennis players, we don't travel together and stay at the same hotels, and we meet only on the track. But Niki Lauda, my so-called 'arch rival' when I won the World Championship, has always been a very good friend.

"To many people he comes across as cold and clinical, but he's not at all a cold fish and I believe that the appalling accident in the German Grand Prix at Nurburgring in 1976 (just before our battle royal) has made him much more outgoing and confident.

"He defeated death in hospital entirely ▶

Three-time Formula One World Champion Lewis Hamilton listening intently to Lauda at the 2014 Abu Dhabi Grand Prix

by his own hard work. It was a superhuman performance."

For his part, Lauda was just as complimentary and friendly towards Hunt.

"There are good drivers and bad ones and then there are the really talented ones who are difficult to beat and James was one of them," he said.

"We respected each other very much because, in the old days, to drive 300kph side by side towards a corner, if someone makes a mistake, one or both are killed. Hunt was someone you could rely on to be really precise."

The 2013 Hollywood film Rush dramatised Hunt and Lauda's relationship and, although Hunt did indeed label Lauda as "The Rat" due to his features, the Austrian knows it was all in good jest.

"Off the circuit, if I had a beer with someone it would be James," he said.

"We were competitors but there was no hate. He called me 'The Rat' as it is in the film, but it was a joke. [Only] on the track we were enemies."

It seems incredible that throughout all the pressure both men were under during 1976 they could still find the time to share a beer – and perhaps a hushed chat – about the dangers, perils and glory available in their chosen profession.

In one sense, though, their friendship makes perfect sense.

With the eyes of the world watching their titanic battle for the Formula One World Championship, who could understand the pressure on Hunt better than his main adversary and vice versa?

"I wanted Niki to be well and racing again," Hunt recalled. "I didn't want to beat him while he was lying in a hospital bed."

HEAD-TO-HEAD FACT FILE:

NIKI LAUDA

D.O.B: 22/02/1949
NATIONALITY: Austrian
GRAND PRIX CAREER: 1971-79, 82-85
WINS: 25
PODIUM FINISHES: 54
WORLD CHAMPION: 1975, 1977, 1984

JAMES HUNT

D.O.B: 29/08/1947
NATIONALITY: British
GRAND PRIX CAREER: 1973-79
WINS: 10
PODIUM FINISHES: 23
WORLD CHAMPION: 1976

"JAMES'S WIN BROUGHT AN ENORMOUS AMOUNT OF ATTENTION TO HIM AND TO THE SPORT IN GENERAL... IT WAS A COMPLETELY NEW EXPERIENCE FOR A BRITISH CHAMPION TO BE TREATED LIKE THIS"

Hunt was the ultimate sporting heart-throb

A LIFE LIVED AT FULL SPEED

Britain had a new World Champion – and Hunt was in demand like never before...

Immediately after winning the World Championship, Hunt professed that he found it difficult to comprehend that his dream had come true. Equally, he appeared to struggle to understand how much his life was about to change.

"I wasn't particularly aware of being any sort of hero to the British fans because I was living in Spain at the time," Hunt had said after his Brands Hatch win.

"I wasn't spending much time in England. That season I'd obviously become bigger news, but I wasn't really aware of it."

Hunt was mobbed at Heathrow Airport when he returned from Japan and it did not take him long to realise that life would never quite be the same again.

He had gone from being merely a contender to a World Champion and he joined an elite list of British sportsman containing only Mike Hawthorn, Graham Hill, Jim Clark, John Surtees and Jackie Stewart. Of that list, Hunt was by far the

Hunt winning Daily Express Sportsman of the Year in 1976 alongside Sportswoman of the Year, showjumper Debbie Johnsey

Hunt with former wife Suzy and Hollywood star Richard Burton

most photogenic and quotable and he was in high demand from public and press alike.

Hunt, along with fellow speed merchant Barry Sheene – the 1976 500cc World Champion on two wheels – had become a true media darling and Hunt's personality meant he thoroughly enjoyed the spoils of victory, whether they be picking up awards or by confirming his status as Britain's most eligible batchelor.

Event seemed to follow event in no time at all for Hunt following his success.

One that particularly stands out is the day held at Brands Hatch in tribute to Hunt on November 7.

The engraver had barely finished adding Hunt's name to the list of World Champions and thousands showed up to try and grab a photo, an autograph and maybe even a peck on the cheek from Britain's hottest property.

Incredibly enough, and further proof of their friendship, Hunt was not the only man in demand at Brands Hatch on that bright day as Niki Lauda himself – Hunt's so-called nemesis – also flew in for the event, although a planned autograph signing session never got going due to the number of fans present.

On December 14, a potential public speed bump was well manoeuvred by Hunt as he met former wife Suzy and Richard Burton, the Hollywood star and now her husband, at a Mayfair event.

Hunt was all smiles in the photographs and he was similarly as pleased for Suzy and Richard in private. It was not an act. He was delighted his first wife had found somebody.

ABOVE: Hunt was extremely
photogenic and the public
could not get enough of his
dashing looks

"He's a very nice guy," Hunt said of the Welshman.

"He called himself my father-in-law, and he's been a very nice father-in-law to me ever since. They looked at that time as though they were good for each other, and that situation suited me fine, them fine, and everyone was happy.

"We didn't have any divorce hassles at all, which can sometimes turn very nasty, and our marriage ended on very good terms indeed. She was happy. I was happy, Richard was happy – everything turned out beautifully."

Hunt's feet barely touched the ground in the months that followed his World Championship win as his trophy cabinet swelled with awards and plaudits from far and wide, including the British Racing Drivers Club and the Sports Writers'

Association, although the BBC Sports Personality of the Year award eluded him, going to 1976 World and Olympic figure skating champion John Curry.

It was a whirlwind time in a whirlwind life that brought Hunt the kind of acclaim never before witnessed in Formula One.

"James's win brought an enormous amount of attention to him and to the sport in general," Murray Walker, the hugely respected commentator, said. "It was a completely new experience for a British champion to be treated like this.

"All the respected motoring magazines were used to recording victories and news from on the track, but James was the first champion to become popular with the daily press. He was under the microscope like nobody before him and he was extremely famous and popular."

> HE WAS UNDER THE MICROSCOPE LIKE NOBODY BEFORE AND HE WAS EXTREMELY POPULAR

Hunt was great friends with Barry
Sheene, another fantastic racer, if
on two wheels rather than four.
The pair were kindred spirits,
perhaps because they could well
understand the dangers the other
endured in their chosen profession

Hunt and his McLaren M26 in the pits with McLaren chief Teddy Mayer (left) and team manager Alastair Caldwell (centre), 1978

"WE HAD DRAMA AFTER DRAMA. WE HAD SUZY LEAVING JAMES, WE HAD NIKI'S BAD CRASH, THE BRANDS HATCH DISQUALIFICATION – INCIDENT AFTER INCIDENT JUST WENT ON, IT WAS RIDICULOUS REALLY! IT MADE FOR AN INTERESTING SEASON, THAT'S FOR SURE"

"NEVER BORING"

Alastair Caldwell rose from being a cleaner with McLaren to team manager. In this exclusive interview, he recalls Hunt's incredible season, the battles with Ferrari, the tensions in Japan and dancing on tables with the future champion of the world...

Few people can challenge James Hunt's McLaren story when it comes to the remarkable and the ridiculous. However, Alastair Caldwell's own rise through the ranks with the team pushes Hunt close and he would go on, along with McLaren boss Teddy Mayer, to be the man most responsible for Hunt's thrilling success in 1976.

Caldwell is the man best equipped to immediately take up the story, starting with his own amazing tale of how he returned from New Zealand as a car-obsessed young man determined to break into Formula One.

"I started as a cleaner at McLaren in 1967," he said. "They had no jobs as a mechanic, but I wanted to get inside the building.

"I was as a cleaner for one day because I worked into the night with the official race mechanics, showing them that I knew my stuff, and the next day I was a race mechanic.

"I then went from race mechanic to chief mechanic to racing manager and then, in 1972, I was made team manager.

"We won the World Championship in 1974 with Emerson Fittipaldi, we were runners-up in 1975 and then we won it again with James the year after."

What did he think of James when he first broke onto the scene with Hesketh Racing? Was he put off by the razzamatazz that followed the team around or did he think Hunt had something special?

Caldwell admits he had no idea what to make of Hunt - and whether or not he was champion material.

"Race drivers stick to their race teams, they always have done and they always will do," Caldwell said.

"That means you don't really know how good the driver is because it is the team and the car that is actually the crucial difference.

"A very good driver will not show in a bad race team and vice versa. It's very difficult for a race driver to overcome his team or his car if they are bad.

"That means it was very difficult to assess how good James was because we didn't know how good the car was or how good the team was.

"He seemed to have a lot of talent and they gave an outside appearance of flippancy, but they were a serious team and they did quite well.

"They won in Holland by stopping at the wrong time - God smiled on them in Holland! - so we thought he was pretty good, but we couldn't really know how good until he joined us himself."

What does Caldwell recall about the way McLaren recruited Hunt? Again, he takes up the tale with relish.

BELOW: Caldwell went from being a cleaner at McLaren to team manager, guiding both Emerson Fittipaldi and James to the World Championship

"At the end of 1975, Fittipaldi sprung a surprise when he announced he was off to sign for the Copersucar-sponsored Fittipaldi Automotive team," Caldwell said.

"He had threatened to repeatedly leave but McLaren had not taken his threats seriously, believing they were just a negotiating ploy.

"We were suddenly without a driver and James was also out of a drive. He rang me up out of the blue and said, 'I think I'm your new driver.' I said, 'I think so. You better talk to Teddy [Mayer] about the money, but it won't be much'. And it wasn't much!

"We took him to Silverstone for testing and it was an English spring – and therefore snowing. It was miserably cold and he couldn't fit in the car because his legs were too long! We had to chop the

end of his shoes off and move the bulkhead and brakes forward so he could even get inside the car.

"We had absolutely no idea how quick he was because we barely had any time, so we went to Interlagos for the first race with James as an unknown entity.

"We thought he'd be good but we didn't know until we got there – and then he proved to be very quick."

Hunt, of course, grabbed pole position for the race, quelling any McLaren fears about his ability. It seemed pretty clear; give Hunt the tools and he will finish the job.

Caldwell added: "I remember Jochen [Mass, Hunt's McLaren team-mate] saying to me on the plane to Brazil, 'Who is the number one?' I told him that the fastest car would be the No.1 driver.

"That was the only criteria. It didn't matter

what was written on your car or your forehead – the quickest driver was No.1. And, after practice in Brazil, it was clear that James was quickest and would be No.1.

"He was on pole with no testing at all. It turned out James was very quick indeed and we were very pleased with our choice."

Hunt was notorious for being ill before a race, such were his nerves, and Caldwell accepts the driver could be a loose cannon due to the tension and expectations.

In other words, if events did not go as planned for Hunt when he was in the cockpit, steer clear for a while.

"He'd be sat on the grid and you would think the car was running because it was vibrating so much," Caldwell said.

"The engine was off, though – it was James rattling and shaking the chassis. He had a huge adrenaline reserve and that often got him into trouble because if he came to a sudden stop or halt he had enormous amounts of adrenaline pumping around him, he couldn't control himself.

"He had a habit of throwing up before a race. He would go behind a wall or use a bucket – the boys would find a bucket from somewhere – and off he would go.

"It was interesting. I had a driver in James who was supposed to show no fear because he was English and I'd had Fittipaldi, who was supposed to be a passionate Brazilian, but the opposite was the truth.

"Fittipaldi was so relaxed he would go to sleep in the car on the grid, but James was very wired before a race. He thought about the dangers a bit and I think that's what made him stop. Most don't think of the downsides, but I think James did."

As the 1976 season progressed, it became clear that it was a year like no other. It could not have ebbed and flowed any more, it could not have contained more drama, legal issues, near tragedies and excitement.

"The season was unreal, almost surreal," Caldwell said. "We had drama after drama. We had Suzy leaving James, we had Niki's bad crash, the Brands Hatch disqualification – incident after incident just went on, it was ridiculous really! It made for an interesting season, that's for sure.

"At the end of the season we said that if anyone tried to use it as a film script they'd be laughed out of the office. Yet, it was all true."

Brands Hatch, of course, was the scene of

The champagne flowed at the end of the 1976 British Grand Prix, but the race was dogged by legal controversy that Caldwell did his best to beat

" THE SEASON WAS UNREAL, ALMOST SURREAL. AT THE END OF THE SEASON WE SAID THAT IF ANYONE TRIED TO USE IT AS A FILM SCRIPT THEY'D BE LAUGHED OUT OF THE OFFICE. YET, IT WAS ALL TRUE "

ABOVE: James crosses the line at Brands Hatch in 1976

one of the biggest controversies over the decision to allow Hunt to race following an incident on the first lap.

His car was severely damaged and officials ruled that back-up cars would not be allowed, meaning Hunt looked to be out of the race.

In the pits, Caldwell knew that he had to do something and played a wonderful move.

He simultaneously argued McLaren's case while quietly getting the team's mechanics to fix Hunt's original car, delaying the Formula One bureaucrats long enough to patch it up.

Hunt was back in business and won the race before being subsequently disqualified later in the season.

Caldwell said: "I took a look at the car and decided it couldn't be repaired, but I set in motion the guys to try and repair it.

"McLaren and Ferrari then started arguing that back-up cars should be allowed in the race. The officials argued that would be against the rules, but we all argued.

"I simply said, 'We will take our car off the grid and use our back-up', but meanwhile I was running back to the garage and supervising the repair of the original car.

"When that was finished, I drove it onto the grid myself and then ran back to the meeting and said, 'We've taken our back-up off the grid.' Ferrari immediately realised what I'd done and were mortified.

"They think to this day we colluded with the organisers to get the race delayed but we didn't – I simply joined in with their argument that back-up cars should be allowed.

"I never said, 'We need half an hour to fix the car', we just got that time back anyhow because we delayed them from making a decision.

"I daren't tell Teddy what we were doing because he wouldn't have been able to resist telling everyone we were working on the first car. It was as big a surprise to him as anybody."

Caldwell added that this left Ferrari "enraged" and claimed: "We were then disqualified later on totally spurious grounds."

He explained: "James won the British Grand Prix in his original car, there was absolutely nothing wrong with what he did. He was still racing when the race was stopped – the video of the race still shows him moving when it was called off.

"It was an amazingly fraught season with all kinds of happenings going on – it didn't need any exaggeration, that's for sure."

WE STILL THOUGHT WE WERE TOO FAR OFF SO WE JUST WENT DRINKING AND PARTYING AGAIN. AT ONE POINT, I WAS ON A TABLE WITH HIM DANCING

By the time Hunt arrived in Canada for the third-last race of the season, he was back in contention, but then the hammer blow was delivered that he was now disqualified from the British Grand Prix. Lauda was handed Hunt's extra three points and the Englishman again had a mountain to climb.

It would be unfair to say that Hunt and Caldwell gave up the chase but, essentially, they did not think there was a chance they could now overtake Lauda.

Instead, they decided to party.

"James was professional enough, but when we got to Canada, we were testing and we got the news that we had lost the British Grand Prix points," he said.

"That made us all very bitter. We had won it fair and square and we were angry that we had the points taken away from us. We didn't give up, but we decided not to care anymore.

"There was a very good band on in the huge bar at the hotel we stayed in and we got back from the track the night before the race. We all got p***ed and James kept disappearing with the lead singer in between her sets. We were sitting there partying, she would finish her performance, disappear to their room for a while and then come back down and carry on singing.

"This carried on all evening and eventually I went to bed at midnight. James was still drinking and at 7am he was still there, totally dishevelled with the same girl. He then got in his car and won the race."

It was back on. Just. But still Hunt and Caldwell thought it was unlikely, so they decided to treat the Watkins Glen Grand Prix with a similarly laissez-faire attitude.

"We did the same at Watkins Glen," Caldwell said. "We still thought we were too far off so we just went drinking and partying again.

"At one point, I was on a table with him dancing. He was staying in the Seneca Lodge motel and came to my hotel where I was staying and we'd just have a drink and a party.

"He had to travel back to this motel, got there at some stage and then – again – the next day he got to the track in a dishevelled state and won the race! Now we had 18 points from two races and it was all looking possible again. We then got deadly serious."

So then, to Japan.

"James and Niki both vehemently argued that it shouldn't be held," Caldwell recalled.

"They were in the office for hours insisting it should not be raced while I was there saying, 'Don't be mad, of course it should be raced.'

"The pair of them were the representatives of the driving committee and they were unwavering on this. It's interesting that James was willing to not race because it was too wet. In the end, we did race, though – and the rest is history.

"Race drivers all basically think they're immortal and are willing to do stupid things. Niki was the bravest one, of course, because he was brave enough to stop.

"He said he would do two laps and stop if it was too dangerous. Fittipaldi

did something similar, although this is widely forgotten.

"Niki pulling into the pits after the second lap wasn't an instinctive thing, it wasn't a surprise, Niki had discussed it."

Lauda's retirement gave Hunt the chance he needed – simply finishing third would now be enough. In Caldwell's opinion, though, he almost blew it by not keeping his tyres cool enough on the rapidly drying Fuji circuit.

"We never discussed it at any length, but he would not cool his tyres or look at his pit board," Caldwell said.

"We were screaming and shouting at him to try and get him to come in, but he wasn't far enough ahead to bring him in and change his tyres. We had to just leave him out there, try and get him to cool his tyres and hope they would last.

"He drove his tyres away to nothing, literally. When he finally came in with just a few laps left he had two flat tyres, the front and rear left side.

"This made it hard to jack the car up as we were set up for one flat tyre, not

two, but we changed the wheels, sent him out on a new set of wets and the rest is history. By sheer serendipity we ended up third."

Third was enough. Hunt had done it.

"It was a great result for James and for us and we were, of course, delighted," Caldwell said.

And what does he make of those events of 40 years ago now? How does he look back on his time managing Hunt, and managing the most incredible season of all.

"I'm not that deep a thinker and I'm no Murray Walker," Caldwell said.

"I simply just enjoyed James's company. The thing about James is that he was never boring. Ever. Being with and around James was always exciting.

"One thing I like to say is that if James had been stood in a wet bus shelter in Bognor Regis on a Sunday night, he could've made it exciting. He could make things happen. He was total box office."

Indeed he was – and Caldwell was not too bad either...

BUILT FOR SPEED

See how Hunt's World Championship-winning M23 compares to a 21st century successor...

JAMES HUNT

WON 6 RACES DURING THE 1976 SEASON

SPAIN • FRANCE • GERMANY
HOLLAND • CANADA
USA WATKINS GLEN

1976
F1 WORLD CHAMPIONSHIP-WINNING CAR

M23

PRINCIPAL DRIVERS HUNT/MASS

ENGINE **FORD COSWORTH DFV**

WHEELBASE **2718MM**

HEIGHT 914MM

LENGTH 4191MM

WIDTH 2083MM

WEIGHT 587KG

POWER OUTPUT 465BHP

CUBIC CAPACITY 2993CC

 M7A 1968   M23 1974   M23 1976   M26 1977   MP4/1 1981   MP4/2 1984   MP4/2B 1985   MP4/2C 1986   MP4/4 1988   MP4/5 1989

McLAREN EVOLUTION TIMELINE

LEWIS HAMILTON

WON 5 RACES DURING THE 2008 SEASON

AUSTRALIA · MONACO
UK · GERMANY · CHINA

2008
F1 WORLD CHAMPIONSHIP-WINNING CAR

MP4-23

PRINCIPAL DRIVERS HAMILTON/KOVALAINEN

ENGINE MERCEDES-BENZ F0108V V8

HEIGHT 1100MM

WHEELBASE 3188MM

LENGTH 4775MM

WIDTH 1795MM

WEIGHT 600KG

POWER OUTPUT 765BHP

CUBIC CAPACITY 2398CC

Source: www.mclaren.com

MP4/6 1991 | MP4/7 1992 | MP4/8 1993 | MP4-12 1997 | MP4-13 1998 | MP4-14 1999 | MP4-17D 2003 | MP4-20A 2005 | MP4-23 2008

A TREASURE HUNT

We open the vaults to take an exclusive look at some of the priceless and timeless items from James Hunt's Formula One racing career...

I n a downstairs snooker room in Tom and Freddie's home in Sussex there lies a treasure trove of Formula One memorabilia and memories.

Stored carefully in boxes and only rarely shown in public, Tom and Freddie have still got priceless reminders of their father's racing career.

From his 1976 McLaren racesuit – that famous deep, rich red as bright as ever – to his beloved briefcase, they have kept the lot.

The items offer a real sense of the era – including the oil stains that still sit on Hunt's racesuit and the briefcase contents, complete with Hunt's squash sweatbands, business papers and the annual minutes from the AGM at Sunningdale Golf Club, the Berkshire club that Hunt often played.

On the pages that follow, take a sneak peek at the items that made Hunt such an iconic figure, study the remarkably basic looking steering wheel that guided him to glory and grab a glimpse of the man behind the public persona.

Marlboro

TEXACO

JAM HUN

BELL

VE$C-R

KEEPING YOUR HEAD

Adorned with the colours of his alma mater, Wellington College, this is the helmet Hunt wore during the 1976 season. A design classic and instantly recognisable

HESKETH RACING JACKET

Hesketh Racing's all-white uniform, complete with patriotic blue and red stripes to represent the Union flag, helped them stand out – as did their ability to party as hard as they raced

AN ICONIC COLOUR, AN ICONIC SEASON

You know your job is on the wrong side of risky when you have your blood type sewn into your uniform. Hunt's 1976 McLaren racesuit had 'A Rh+' stitched onto it to let medics know in case of an emergency. The racesuit is surprisingly heavy and bulky due to the amount of fireproof materials needed to try and keep him safe. It is no wonder he finished each race drenched in sweat and would regularly lose up to 10 pounds per Grand Prix due to the exertion involved in controlling his car

BRIEFCASE ENCOUNTER

This briefcase was a gift to James from Texaco in 1976 as a reward for him being "an outstanding World Champion". He used it frequently, often attending meetings with his thumb holding the broken catch closed!

PLENTY TO SMILE ABOUT

Compared to today's Formula One technology, Hunt's McLaren steering wheel looks almost primitive, but that did not stop him in 1976

JAMES HUNT
ジェームス ハント

1976 JAPAN GRAND PRIX TROPHY

It may stand barely 20cm high, but this is the ornamental vase trophy that changed Hunt's life. It was his reward for coming third in Japan

1976 GERMAN GRAND PRIX TROPHY

It was the scariest race of the 1976 season following Niki Lauda's crash and this small, wood-mounted trophy was Hunt's prize for a brilliantly executed race

A DIFFERENT KIND OF BUBBLES

This golden magnum of champagne from renowned makers Moet & Chandon was just one of hundreds of gifts and mementoes Hunt was given in the years that followed his World Championship success

1976 DUTCH GRAND PRIX TROPHY

Hunt's second consecutive win at Zandvoort really gave his season the impetus and momentum it needed and he never really looked back. His win at the same circuit the year before represented his finest moment with Hesketh Racing

MAN'S BEST FRIEND

Oscar was Hunt's adored companion when he lived in Spain. When he opened a nightclub he called it Oscar's in tribute to his favourite pet

BLOWING HIS OWN TRUMPET...

Hunt learned the instrument at school and even played at the Royal Albert Hall in the lead up to the 1976 British Grand Prix

WHITE TIME TO RETIRE

Hunt finished his Formula One career back in white – just as he had started with Hesketh, but this time it was for Walter Wolf Racing. This racesuit is from his final season in 1979

Hunt picks a unique
way to cool down
during the 1976
season

BACK *TO* BACK?

James Hunt could not wait for the 1977 season to begin and neither could the waiting world. Could Britain's most charismatic sportsman repeat his success?

James Hunt started the 1977 season at the very pinnacle of his career.

It was literally impossible for the Englishman to get any higher in his chosen profession.

The No.1 proudly emblazoned on the nose of his McLaren said it all. Hunt was officially the fastest and best Formula One driver on the planet.

Hunt could not wait to get the 1977 season underway after spending most of the time following his Fuji win picking up awards, attending events (in jeans and T-shirt, to much harrumphing from the tie-and-blazer brigade) and keeping McLaren sponsors Marlboro happy at a series of promotional events.

"Driving and racing again was like finding an oasis in the desert," Hunt said when referring to the start of the 1977 season.

"You have to understand that winning is like a drug. It certainly had that effect on me. I wanted more. It was addictive – I'd done very little winning before and this seemed like a reward for all the hard work."

Off the track, Jane Birbeck, a blonde who was to become his long-time companion following Hunt's divorce from Suzy, began to play an increasing role in his life and she often showed up at Grands Prix with Hunt.

Unfortunately, she was to be a first-hand witness to two seasons that never really got going for the 1976 World Champion.

Hunt's season got off to a bad start in his M23 in Argentina as suspension troubles ended his race as he was leading – an occurrence that was to become a

19

Mirror Sport
Telephone: (STD code 01)—353 0246

SUPER DART!

Scheckter wins Grand Prix opener

HUNT GOES CRASHING

From MIRROR REPORTER in Buenos Aires

JAMES HUNT, Britain's world motor-racing champion, sensationally crashed out of the Argentinian Grand Prix yesterday when he was in the lead.

LEIGHTON TOLD —TAKE A REST

Security

JOHN BATTLES TO SETTLE HIS DEBT
By DAVE HORRIDGE

Roscoe warning for Wimbledon

SIX-WICKET COPE STAKES HIS CLAIM
From PETER LAKER in Nagpur

JAMES HUNT . . . lost his chance in the 31st lap.

TOMORROW: THE TOP POOLS SERVICE BY LONGSIGHT

JAMES HUNT 107

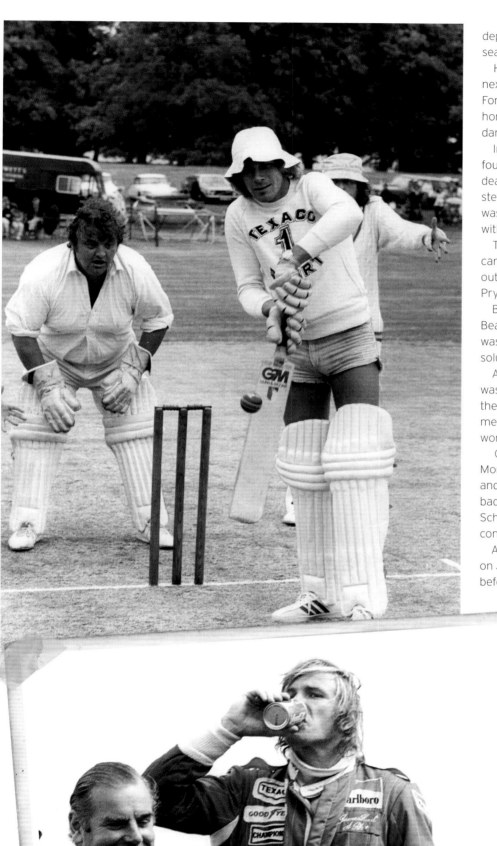

depressingly common issue across the season.

He hit back with second place in the next Grand Prix in Brazil before the Formula One world was given another horrendous reminder of just how dangerous the sport could be.

In South Africa, where Hunt came fourth, the race was overshadowed by the death of Tom Pryce and a teenage steward, Frederik Jansen van Vuuren, who was killed when Pryce's Shadow collided with him.

The fire extinguisher Van Vuuren was carrying on his way to attempting to put out a fire in Renzo Zorzi's engine struck Pryce in the head and killed him instantly.

By the time the season got to Long Beach for the US Grand Prix West, Hunt was all ready off the pace but a potential solution was around the corner.

After coming seventh in America, Hunt was in a new vehicle, the McLaren M26, for the Spanish Grand Prix but, if anything, his mechanical problems were about to get worse rather than better.

Consecutive retirements in Spain and Monaco, plus difficult showings in Belgium and Sweden, meant Hunt was struggling badly and well off Niki Lauda and Jody Scheckter, who were clearly the two main contenders for the World Championship.

A third place at the French Grand Prix on July 3 was a welcome podium return before Hunt had the highlight of the season on home soil, winning the British Grand Prix for a second consecutive year (give or take the legal wranglings that so beset his 1976 victory).

Northern Ireland's John Watson set the running that day and Hunt did his best to chase him down to no avail until, fortunately for Hunt, Watson's car malfunctioned, gifting the win to Hunt. He enjoyed his return to ⊙

" WE JUST HAD A VERY BAD RUN OF LUCK AND, FOR THE MOST PART, A LOUSY CAR "

winning ways, but they were not to last.

In Germany and Austria his car let him down; in Holland, Hunt collided with Mario Andretti, ending his afternoon, and in Italy he pushed his luck once too often and had to retire after a bad spin.

His bad luck was punctuated by another win, at the United States Grand Prix East at Watkins Glen, where he repeated his superb victory from the year before, but another incident at the Canadian Grand Prix highlighted that it was not to be a happy year for Hunt.

The British driver was leading when he had a terrifying crash with Jochen Mass which led to his retirement and the infamous punch he threw at a race marshall who tried to spirit him away from his broken car.

While punching a marshall can never be justified, it at least showed the pressure Hunt was under and the pressure he put himself under to try and perform.

There was no doubt about it, Hunt's defence of his title was going badly awry due to a variety of issues – mostly mechanical and therefore out of his control.

His notorious temper was never far away, particularly as witnessed in Canada, although a win in the final race of the season in Japan assuaged Hunt somewhat and proved that he was as good as ever when he could get the most out of his car.

The facts spoke for themselves, though.

He finished fifth in the World Championship with 40 points as Lauda took the honours.

In a bitter irony for Hunt, he felt he was actually driving as well as he had done the year before but too many mechanical issues – plus several self-confessed driving errors – undermined his title defence.

"We just had a very bad run of luck and, for the most part, a lousy car," Hunt recalled.

"I was driving even better than in 1976, obviously with more confidence.

"I won three races in that car and broke down three times in sight of victory.

"Niki won the Championship with only three wins."

ABOVE: Hunt gets into celebration mode after winning the United States Grand Prix East at Watkins Glen during the 1977 season

1978

NEVER GIVE UP

1977 had proved to be a difficult year for Hunt and the season that followed was even more of a challenge, yet he persevered in a bid to return to winning ways

If Hunt had to wrestle an unco-operative car and bad fortune during the 1977 season, life in 1978 proved to be even more testing.

His McLaren M26 was off the pace and Hunt was to eventually finish the season with just eight points after a serious of incidents – and further tragedy.

Hunt escaped from the pressure he was under by returning as often as possible to Spain, where he continued to spend as much time as possible with Jane and his beloved dog Oscar.

On the track, 1978 started with fourth place in Argentina and, depressingly enough for Hunt, that was almost the highlight of the season.

Accidents in Brazil, Long Beach and Belgium ensured plenty of headlines, while retirements in South Africa and Monaco caused further frustrations.

Hunt had always been in motor racing to win, or at least to be competing to win, so his failure to grab the public's imagination at the 1978 British Grand Prix must have been particularly painful.

Unlike the previous two years, where Hunt had left the crowds on the verge of hysteria following two magnificent wins, 1978 saw him spin off early on.

More disappointments followed in Germany and Austria, he finished 10th in the Dutch Grand Prix on August 27 and then came the season's defining, tragic moment – and more evidence of Hunt's astonishing personal courage.

Swedish driver Ronnie Peterson was a popular man in the pit lane with mechanics and other drivers alike. He had proven his driving merit over an eight-year Formula One career and he and Hunt were friends.

At Monza for the Italian Grand Prix on September 10, an issue with the starting lights at the beginning of the race meant some cars had a rolling start, giving them precious speed advantage over those in front of them.

That meant that when the field hit the first corner, the cars were more bunched up than usual and, in the ensuing melee, Hunt had nowhere to go after Riccardo Patrese squeezed him for space. Hunt touched Peterson's Lotus, which then hit the right-hand barriers hard and the Swede's car immediately became engulfed in flames.

BELOW: Hunt was determined to prove that 1978 could be better than the season before

DAILY Mirror

INSIDE TODAY'S MIRROR
FLASH! BANG! WALLOP!

Monday, September 11, 1978   8p

James saves race ace from blazing car

INFERNO: With crashed cars littering the track, worried drivers and officials race towards Ronnie Peterson's blazing Lotus.

HERO HUNT

MODEST: Crash hero James Hunt

BRITISH driver James Hunt was the hero of a spectacular ten-car crash which injured two top aces in the Italian Grand Prix yesterday.

Helped by another driver, Hunt risked his life to save Ronnie Peterson of Sweden from his blazing Lotus.

From
PATRICK MENNEM
in Monza

Seconds afterwards, the car became an inferno.

Both, Peterson and Italy's Vittorio Brambilla were in critical condition in hospital last night.

Start

Peterson, 34, who lives in Berkshire with his wife and daughter, has multiple fractures of his legs, a fractured pelvis and scorched lungs.

Brambilla, 40, was even

more badly hurt, with a fractured skull and probable brain damage.

The pile-up came soon after the start of the race at Monza.

As the drivers were jockeying for position on the harrowing track, a car cannoned into 30-year-old Hunt's McLaren.

Hunt, in turn, went into Peterson, and a split second later ten cars littered the track.

Hunt saw Peterson struggling to free himself from the burning Lotus and dashed to help him.

He kicked Peterson's seat belt free and aided by Switzerland's Clay

RESCUER: Regazzoni   VICTIM: Peterson

Regazzoni, pulled him from the car just before it went up.

Hunt insisted afterwards that he was no hero. But he did add modestly: "A marshall had damped some of the flames down, but the car was still burning as we tried to pull him out.

"His legs were trapped under the steering wheel and it was very difficult to free him."

Action

Because of Hunt's action, Peterson's burns were minor. He will be out of racing for at least a year.

West German driver Hans Stuck received minor injuries in the pile-up.

The race was started again nearly three hours later and was won by Austria's Niki Lauda, who narrowly escaped death in a crash two years ago.

PICTURE SPECIAL—See Page 3

LEFT: Hunt shrugged off the plaudits following his attempts to save Ronnie Peterson's life

BOTTOM: Left to right, Ronnie Peterson, race winner Mario Andretti, Patrick Depailler and James Hunt in conversation at the Argentine Grand Prix track, January 1978

With a fuel tank filled with high-octane petrol, the fireball that consumed Peterson's car was terrifying.

What happened next, though, was truly remarkable.

Hunt immediately sensed that Peterson, his friend, was in serious trouble, so stopped his own car and raced head on into the inferno.

As thick black smoke and flames roared out, Hunt dived in and managed to wrestle the badly injured Peterson out of the vehicle. At any point the car could have exploded, but Hunt, along with a marshall, ignored the risks.

"I saw a car on fire behind me and nothing much going on," Hunt told the Associated Press, complete with a typically British stiff upper lip. "So I went to go and have a look and see what was going on.

"His car was in a bad state and he was still half in it. One marshall who had arrived did a terrific job. He had one extinguisher and rather than blast the whole thing off in an attempt to put out 40 gallons of fuel, he was conserving it.

"He [Peterson] was trapped by his foot. ▶

Ronnie Peterson (right, yellow racesuit) is attended to on the track as James Hunt (white racesuit) looks on with concern following Peterson's terrible incident in Monza, which tragically proved to be fatal

We eventually managed to get the steering wheel bent, got him freed off and got him away."

Hunt's actions were remarkably, fantastically brave. They showed Formula One at its very best – and also its most dangerous. It might be an exaggeration to suggest there was a huge esprit de corps among different teams, but no driver wanted to see another hurt or killed and most hoped that they could count on their rivals to help them out.

Hunt had more than done his part but, unfortunately, it turned out to be in vain.

Peterson had shattering injuries to his legs – surgeons counted more than 25 fractures – and although his condition was initially stable, complications arising from the fractures in his thighs caused fat clots which starved him of oxygen, effectively leaving him brain dead.

It is arguable that it was at this point Hunt felt his time in Formula One was up.

Seventh in the United States East Grand Prix at Watkins Glen – previously a happy hunting ground – and then a final accident in the Canadian Grand Prix brought Hunt's season to an end.

It also marked the end of his time with McLaren.

Hunt had been in discussions with Walter Wolf, an Austrian-born millionaire hoping to bankroll his Formula One team to glory.

Having been a close witness to Niki Lauda's crash in 1976 and then the hero

of the hour in pulling Peterson free of his car, Hunt had seen his fair share of sobering moments, but Wolf's offer was too good to ignore.

And, although the 1979 season offered hope of a fresh start, Hunt was actually within months of hanging his racesuit up for good.

Hunt in deep conversation with
Bernie Ecclestone, then owner of
the Brabham team, at the Swedish
Grand Prix, June 1978

Even a racing driver needs to clean his racesuit every now and again. Here is Hunt's hanging on his balcony in Canada, October 1976

ON HIS TERMS

JAMES HUNT RETIRED HALFWAY THROUGH THE 1979 SEASON AFTER HIS WOLF CAR REPEATEDLY LET HIM DOWN. IT WAS TIME FOR HIM TO WALK AWAY WITH HIS MOST VALUED PRIZE - HIS HEALTH

James Hunt had never hidden his intentions to cut and run from Formula One the moment his desire to take part had evaporated.

After the difficulties surrounding the 1977 and 1978 seasons, when Hunt tussled hard but to little avail at McLaren, the move to Wolf for 1979 did not do him any favours and few would suggest it was anything but a disappointment as his Wolf drive repeatedly failed to last the distance.

Hunt's original plan was to quit after the Watkins Glen Grand Prix in America on October 7 and he announced this publicly well in advance.

However, as the 1979 season ambled along, it occurred to Hunt that he would never be competitive, he would never be elbowing his way to the front of the grid or racing on the edge and so, essentially, what was the point?

Risking your life to win was one thing. Risking your life to come eighth was quite another. In the end, Hunt changed his plans and got out while the going was still good.

After 92 races and 10 wins, his Formula One career came to an end at the Monaco Grand Prix on May 27; the same venue where he had taken part in his first Grand Prix five years, 11 months

and 25 days earlier. Few get to choose their own exit - whether in Formula One or elsewhere - but Hunt was clearly delighted that it was time to go.

In a similar way to Niki Lauda, whose bravery to pull up in the Japan rain three years earlier was so widely admired for its honesty, Hunt's decision bore the hallmarks of a man who knew himself, knew the pressures and dangers he was under and knew that the internal fire to keep competing had been extinguished.

The list of sportsman who have stayed in their chosen profession for too long is a depressing one. The likes of Muhammad Ali, Brian Clough, Alex Higgins and Michael Jordan carried on way after the lights had come on and the music had stopped and there is

always a certain poignancy to see a former great still trying to keep ahead.

Hunt wanted none of that.

"The truth is, I was on the point of retiring at the end of last year," he said.

"I'd made enough money to live on for the rest of my life. I'm not a particularly high liver and I was ready to get out then.

"But I didn't retire as I was getting some criticism from people who accused me of not trying, which really angered me because I was doing my best as I have always done.

"It would seem pretty obvious to me, and anybody who bothered to think about it, that if one is going to take all that risk, it's worth it only for the potential rewards. And that means winning."

Hunt had no regrets about joining Wolf

from McLaren and was drawn to the team because of their desire to break into Formula One's elite club.

Perhaps Hunt saw a touch of Hesketh Racing in his new team.

Perhaps he was determined once again to help the underdogs prove their doubters wrong.

"I had some very good offers for my last year, including one from Ferrari," Hunt revealed. "But the Wolf Racing team looked a natural for me. They were hungry for success and they'd had a taste of it without anything concrete.

"I joined them not because of the car or the offer but because of their enthusiasm and determination.

"Unfortunately and unluckily – because luck is involved – our car ain't quick enough."

Ahead of his final race at Monaco,

Hunt outlined his desire to finish his Formula One career on a glorious high. This, of course, did not come to pass, but it at least underlines the fighting spirit he had demonstrated throughout those 92 races and beyond.

"I'm only in it to win," Hunt said. "Winning is what it is all about."

He was right there: Hunt was a fighter.

He had scrapped his way to the top of his profession – and that should never be forgotten.

"I cannot criticise a world that has given me so much," he added. "I'm just very glad that one year I had a car that was capable of winning the World Championship and that I was able to grab my chance when I had it."

> **IT WOULD SEEM PRETTY OBVIOUS TO ME, AND ANYBODY WHO BOTHERED TO THINK ABOUT IT, THAT IF ONE IS GOING TO TAKE ALL THAT RISK, IT'S WORTH IT ONLY FOR THE POTENTIAL REWARDS. AND THAT MEANS WINNING**

In the following exclusive columns for the Daily Mirror in 1979, Hunt explained the concerns he had about driving at the highest level due to the horrendous safety record and risks involved in Formula One in the 1970s. Hunt was one of his sport's most articulate drivers and he offered a fascinating insight into the psyche required to do the job

THE *HARD* WAY OUT

I am retiring at the end of this year because I have reached the stage in my life when the dangers of my business – and therefore the dangers to my life – outweigh the rewards to be achieved.

Without racing, my normal life expectancy would be, say, 75 years. That means that even if I raced for five more years, driving would still take up only just over 10 per cent of my life.

But five more years, statistically, would give me only an even chance of being around to enjoy the remainder of my 75 years.

You see, I believe that anyone's business or career is – or at least it should be – only a means to an end.

For me, that end is a happy, interesting and well-balanced existence. I now have as much as motor-racing can reasonably give me towards that. So it seems pointless to continue.

Having said that, I should add that there is nothing I would love more than to continue to race until old age or incompetence finally got the better of me – and that could easily be another 15 years.

Instead, I am now taking a big step into a world that is unknown to me.

Let's be quite frank, I have made plenty of money out of racing.

But large piles of money have a habit of disintegrating when not properly looked after, and (apart from receiving cheques) I hate business and money matters.

But in order to live the unlavish, but comfortable, lifestyle to which I have become accustomed, I shall have to work extremely hard at generating income from the pile I have.

So of course it would be easier just to jump into racing cars and let the money roll in.

The HARD way out

I AM retiring at the end of this year because I have reached the stage in my life when the dangers of my business – and therefore the dangers to my life – outweigh the rewards to be achieved.

Without racing, my normal life expectancy would be, say, 75 years. That means that even if I raced for five more years, driving would still take up only just over 10 per cent. of my life.

But five more years, statistically, would give me only an even chance of being around to enjoy the remainder of my 75 years.

You see, I believe that anyone's business or career is – or at least should be – only a means to an end.

Happy

For me, that end is a happy, interesting and well-balanced existence.

I now have as much as motor-racing can reasonably give me. So it seems pointless to continue.

Having said that, I should add that there is nothing I would love more than to continue to race until old age or incompetence finally got the better of me – and that could easily be another 15 years.

Instead, I am now taking the big step into a world that is unknown to me.

Let's be quite frank: I have made plenty of money out of racing.

But large piles of money have a habit of disintegrating when not properly looked after, and (apart from receiving cheques) I hate business and money matters.

But in order to live the unlavish, but comfortable, lifestyle to which I have become accustomed, I shall have to work extremely hard at generating income from the pile I have.

So of course, it would be easier just to jump into racing cars and let the money roll in.

Series edited by PETER DONNELLY

> "I NOW HAVE AS MUCH AS MOTOR-RACING CAN REASONABLY GIVE ME. SO IT SEEMS POINTLESS TO CONTINUE. HAVING SAID THAT, THERE IS NOTHING I WOULD LOVE MORE THAN TO CONTINUE TO RACE UNTIL OLD AGE OR INCOMPETENCE FINALLY GOT THE BETTER OF ME"

ABOVE: Retirement meant Hunt could indulge in his favourite sports at home in Spain such as golf, squash, snooker and tennis

SUBSCRIBE TO *F1 RACING* AND RECEIVE
3 ISSUES FOR £3

SUBSCRIBER BENEFITS

- **GREAT SAVINGS**
  3 issues for just £3 then save 23% on the cover price after your trial ends

- **SPREAD THE COST**
  Pay just £22.99 every six issues

- **FREE P&P**
  Every issue delivered direct to your door

- **EXCLUSIVE DEALS**
  Subscriber-only offers and discounts

Visit **www.themagazineshop.com/f1r/ham16**
OR CALL 0344 8488 826
quoting the promotional code **HAM16P**

DANGER *AND ME*

I THINK ABOUT IT ALL THE TIME – IN THE STREET, IN BED, AT THE SUPERMARKET

I was born a competitor. And from a very early age I was prepared to take on any challenge... so long as I thought I stood a chance of winning.

Whether it was dangerous or not didn't matter. Something that's a bit "daring" always adds appeal for small boys, and it did for me. But these days things have changed because regularly driving racing cars at anything up to 200mph has given me a much more acute sense of danger than most people.

Funnily enough, my years of racing have actually reversed my attitude towards doing dangerous things. Now, quite frankly, I want to walk away from them.

I suppose that all sounds a bit odd to a lot of people.

They may wonder: how can a man who won't risk a little skiing holiday, and even appears more chicken to cross the road than most, hurtle around in racing cars at those tremendous speeds for a great part of his working life? Racing is a different thing altogether for me. It is my business, the job I do best, my whole life – at least for a few more months. And I have learned to live with its dangers.

Those dangers are basically like a cloud over my head. It exists all the time. I am constantly very much aware of it all my life.

And I think about it all the time.

When I'm in the supermarket, walking my dogs, in a street, lying in bed at night. Any place. Any time.

But it's very much a cold, clinical thing. All you can do is say to yourself: "The facts of the matter are that you could get the chop in your very next race." This is a frightening thing, and so you think the whole thing through and weigh up the pros and cons. After doing that you don't then go back and fill yourself with negative thoughts. If I was scared to climb into the car and I was scared to death that I was going to get the chop I wouldn't be able to drive. It would be pointless doing it. Of course, that cloud is very much when you're driving and you think of the dangers then, too.

But I reject those thoughts because they're negative – all I'd do would be to drive slower. Which doesn't make it any safer.

Once you're driving, most of the time you're not having accidents and getting hurt. And, if that moment does arrive, it happens so bloody fast and unexpectedly that it's over in the snap of the fingers.

When a driver is killed or badly hurt, it is obviously dreadful on an emotional level. But as far as one's driving is concerned, it doesn't change anything at all, it merely affirms the dangers.

I wish racing was safer and if it was I wouldn't be retiring for another 10 years.

But my decision is made.

And soon I will be able to start a new life in which danger – apart from those we face in everyday life – plays no part.

> " I WISH RACING WAS A WHOLE LOT SAFER AND IF IT WAS I WOULDN'T BE RETIRING FOR ANOTHER 10 YEARS. BUT MY DECISION IS MADE "

Brabham's Carlos Reutemann and Hunt relax at the Kyalami Ranch Hotel before the South African Grand Prix in March 1975

BEHIND THE MICROPHONE

Following his retirement in 1979, Hunt moved into the BBC commentary box alongside the great Murray Walker. In this exclusive interview, Walker explains their friendship and how life did not always run smoothly...

I f there is one man on the planet whose name is synonymous with Formula One, that person is Murray Walker.

The BBC commentator brought motor racing – on two wheels and four – into the homes of Britain and beyond from 1978 to 2001, although his motor racing commentary career actually started back in 1949.

He would no doubt modestly play down the suggestion that he is a broadcasting icon or a worldwide sporting legend, but make no mistake, that is exactly what he is.

His view from the BBC commentators' booth gave him a decades-long and unique perspective into Formula One and also a certain Mr James Hunt.

The two of them worked side by side for the BBC for 13 years following James's recruitment by head of sport Jonathan Martin and they remained colleagues until James's untimely death in 1993.

During their time together, few got to know Hunt as well as Walker and their trips to all four corners of the globe covering Formula One provided plenty of eyebrow-raising moments.

Canon

SKI
3CCD

WORLD

And, as you would expect from a man who has spent most of his life painting pictures with words, Walker is not short of several sentences on his commentating partner and, admirably, he does not try and revise or brush over several aspects of their relationship which did not always go according to plan.

Walker said: "In 1978 the BBC started doing all the races, in 1979 James retired and the BBC came to me and said, 'In future there will be two commentators. James Hunt is the other.'

"This was unprecedented, because all sport then was done by one commentator, whether that be Peter Alliss, Harry Carpenter, David Coleman, myself – people like that.

"It was unprecedented – and I didn't like it [laughs]! My immediate reaction was, 'I don't like this, he knows nothing about commentating.' So, there was a cautious atmosphere between us.

"I was old enough to be his father and we were completely different chaps. There were elements of him that I didn't get and we were just very different personalities."

Their relationship did, however, grow quickly and happily over the years, helped by Walker's admiration for the Hunt he had watched behind a wheel as much as the Hunt he shared a microphone with.

"Formula One is in its 67th season now," Walker said. "And there has been a number of outstanding seasons, with 1976 most definitely up there. It's undoubtedly one of the most exciting and dramatic.

"James was a complete one-off. There has been nobody else with his personality in the history of Formula One.

"By 1976, he had lost his wildness as a driver – as least in the cockpit! - and you only have to look at the 1976 season to know that he was very, very good indeed.

"One of the greatest of all time? Perhaps not, but he was very, very good. That is not to take anything away from him either because you do not win a World Championship ahead of Niki Lauda and other world-class drivers without being very, very talented."

Walker's admiration for the bravery of Hunt and other drivers of that era also remains undimmed.

He has had to sadly report on several tragic Formula One deaths – perhaps the most widely known being Ayrton Senna's at San Marino in 1994 – so Walker knows exactly what courage it takes to get into a cockpit in the first place.

Walker said: "I've got an immeasurable amount of admiration and respect for those drivers.

"Although they didn't think it would

RIGHT: A line-up of World Champions at the 1990 Australian Grand Prix (back row, left to right) James Hunt, Jackie Stewart, Denny Hulme. (Front row, left to right) Nelson Piquet, Juan Manuel Fangio, Ayrton Senna and Jack Brabham

BELOW: Hunt continued to be a media draw after retiring, telling the Daily Mirror in 1982 how he was glad it was Niki Lauda making a comeback and not himself

JAMES WAS A ONE-OFF. THERE HAS BEEN NOBODY ELSE WITH HIS PERSONALITY IN THE HISTORY OF FORMULA ONE

happen to them – because nobody in their right mind would get into a racing car if they thought they would die – they all knew and understood deep down that it *could* happen to them.

"But they turn a blind eye to it because the desire to race and win and transcends everything else.

"Even now they are placing themselves in conditions of extreme danger. Look at the dreadful accident of Jules Bianchi in Japan in 2014. He was being 'protected' by everything that has improved since Senna died in 1994 but he still died tragically.

"In James's day they were in an infinitely bigger danger of death because it was nowhere near as protective or as sophisticated as they are now and James was very conscious of this.

"James was actually a very highly strung chap with a really fearsome temper. He was very aware of the dangers and his career was not very long at all, which is because he was aware of the dangers he was in.

"Look at Jenson Button: he is in his 17th year now whereas James's career was a lot shorter. He was honest enough, frank enough and decent enough to stand up in public and say he was becoming increasingly conscious of the dangers and he wanted to go on living – or words to that effect.

"I have a gigantic amount of respect for the drivers of today and drivers of the past for their courage and will to win; that's what separates them from me."

Walker and Hunt's relationship developed over the years and their contrasting styles soon got rave reviews from viewers.

Walker was the super-efficient professional, full of research, facts, figures and journalistic competency. Hunt was the exact opposite. Although just as knowledgeable as his older commentary partner, he was far more laid back, more opinionated and more willing to cause a rumpus if he was in the mood to. ▶

That often caused moments of friction and although there was far more laughing than shouting and far more handshakes that punches, Walker happily recalls the dynamic that made their relationship work.

"We were just two completely different types of person," Walker recalled. "That is neither a criticism of me or James; it's just the way we were.

"When we were on air I used to stand in the commentary box on the balls of my feet whereas he would be sat down alongside me, calm and relaxed. We had one microphone between the two of us and that was to make sure we didn't talk over the top of each other. It makes sense, really."

Both Hunt and Walker had a tendency to get carried away with the action, always wanting that one microphone to put across their point of view.

Normally they muddled through in a professional fashion, the viewer unaware that both men wanted to speak.

However, just occasionally, the microphone tug of war took on a life of its own.

"I have to admit, to my shame, that I used to get fired up and enthusiastically wanted to convey to the audience what was going on," Walker said.

"James would put his hand up to show he wanted the microphone – and he wouldn't always get it!

ABOVE: Hunt was always happy to chat and advise the next generation of Formula One drivers. Here he is talking with Alessandro Zanardi at the European Grand Prix, Donington Park, April 1993

"Not an admirable way to be, but there we are. Conversely, I would give it to him when he wasn't expecting it.

"At the British Grand Prix one year, he'd decided that I'd said enough.

"So, as I was on my feet talking excitedly about the action, James sat there, tugged at the wires on the microphone and pulled it from my grip. I was incandescent with rage – really furious, in fact – and I had my fist back to punch him.

"Fortunately, producer Mark Wilkin was wagging his finger at me and we got through it!

"Even though we were so different in personality, background and the rest of it, from the public's point of view our chemistry seemed to work well.

"I would be shouting and screaming with adrenaline falling out of me by the bucketful. Meanwhile, James would be there, all calm and authoritative and – what the British public loved most – outspoken.

"James was prepared to say things as a commentator – by virtue of his background, being World Champion and his personality – that I would never dared have said.

"James was prepared to criticise and vilify drivers if he felt they deserved it and I wasn't – partly because of my personality and partly because I didn't think it was right to criticise somebody for something when I hadn't done it myself."

At their very first Grand Prix in Monaco in 1980, Hunt immediately proved to Walker and the rest of the BBC team – including Wilkin – that he planned to do things his own way.

"Not only did James not care what people thought about what he said, he also didn't care what he looked like – or what people thought he looked like," Walker said.

"He turned up at the Monaco Grand Prix ▶

– the crème de la crème of the circuit – in a scruffy T-shirt, cut-off shorts, no shoes, his leg in a plaster cast from ankle to crotch after a skiing injury and half a bottle of rosé in his hand.

"We sat on these two small park chairs, and James plonked himself down on his chair, put his bad leg on my lap and away we went.

"Halfway through the race he was provided with another bottle of rosé and we did it like that. But that was James! From the public's point of view, it didn't affect the quality of what he said. What he said was always worth listening to."

Walker also gives some insight into life on the road with Hunt in the build-up to the Grands Prix they so enjoyed covering.

"Outside the box, we never shouted or screamed at each other," he said.

"He always travelled and stayed with the McLaren team, rather than the BBC, so he was a spirit apart, if you like.

"I'd be on my feet all the time in the pit lane talking to drivers, mechanics, team principals and engineers, trying to get knowledge, while James would sit in the Marlboro tent drinking with his chums – and everybody would go to James!

"He didn't lack knowledge – the

difference was I had to go and get it – and good luck to him!"

Hunt only once failed to turn up for his commentary duties, during a Belgian Grand Prix.

Walker did the race on his own before finding out what had happened.

He grins in the retelling of the tale.

"In Belgium, he wasn't there five minutes before the race," Walker recalled. "Then, five minutes in, no sign. Then, 30 minutes in, no sign. An hour in, no sign. The entire race, no sign.

"James subsequently appeared and apologised for having not been there on account of the fact he'd been in bed with a stomach complaint.

"And, as I always say, that's the first time I've heard two Belgian nurses called a 'stomach complaint'!"

As with the rest of the racing fraternity, Hunt's death in 1993 left Walker "shell-shocked", but his 13 years in the commentary box had changed the style of television reporting and commentary forever.

Although a few former professionals had made the move into the media before Hunt – Jimmy Hill in football and Richie Benaud in cricket being popular examples

– Formula One had yet to really embrace the concept.

The straight-talking, funny, direct and often controversial Hunt changed all that.

Any Formula One coverage across the world now contains at least one person who has been there, on the grid, in helmet and overalls.

Hunt changed the game.

And changed it for the better.

Yet, the final word, as always, belongs to Walker, who tried to encapsulate who James was – not only as a long-standing colleague but, more importantly, his long-standing friend.

"I had the greatest of affection for James," Walker said. "He had a personality that is unique in the history of Formula One. James really turned Britain on to the sport.

"Before 1976 and James's victory, Britain was not very interested in Formula One. You barely read about it in the sports pages.

"But then James, by his wins and his personality, woke Britain up to Formula One. Formula One actually owes him an enormous amount."

As always, nobody can say it better than Murray Walker.

HUNT AT HOME

During the 1980s and away from the BBC, commentating and enjoying himself in the Marlboro tent, Hunt had various other interests – including a stint as a farmer.

Hunt, having grown tired of life in Spain, bought a huge farm, Park Farm, in Buckinghamshire, where he lived with Jane Birbeck.

The pair eventually split up in 1981, but it would not take long for Hunt to meet his future wife.

Sarah Lomax met Hunt in Spain and the couple married in December 1983, moving in together in a house Hunt bought in Wimbledon Common, not far from high-profile neighbours such as snooker player Jimmy White and Rolling Stones guitarist Ronnie Wood.

Evenings playing snooker – sometimes with Jimmy himself – were interspersed with rounds of golf and Hunt's love of breeding budgies.

His aviary at the Wimbledon house was a source of great affection for Hunt and he loved nothing more than travelling the country entering budgie breeding competitions.

"He got as much pleasure from that as anything else," his sister Sally said. "It brought him great joy."

In September 1985, Hunt's life changed forever when Sarah had a baby boy, Tom. Bubbles Horsley – the man who had gone looking for Hunt to offer him a job at Hesketh more than a decade earlier – was Tom's godfather.

In July 1987, Tom got a beloved baby brother in Freddie.

Eventually, two years later, Hunt and Sarah split up, but not before Hunt had truly taken to fatherhood, a role he grew into even further in the coming years.

"James really was a wonderful father," Murray Walker noted. "When we went to the Portuguese Grand Prix, we stayed in a hotel overlooking a wonderful beach and James took the two boys with him for a week before the race. He loved his sons a huge amount."

The wedding day of James and Sarah Lomax

James Hunt's two sons,
Tom and Freddie, talk
through life with their
father, their pride in his
achievement and
mowing the lawn...

ABOVE: Tom, left, and Freddie with their father's iconic Hesketh Formula One car

James Hunt died of a heart attack in his Wimbledon home on June 15, 1993.

Aged just 45, his death came as an awful, seismic shock and an incalculable loss to his family, friends and loved ones.

"It just seemed unbelievable," Chris Jones said. "It was very sad. And we miss him still."

In the immediate years before his death, Hunt had left behind the cameras and champagne of his younger life and seemed extremely happy.

His stable relationship with Helen Dyson helped - tragically, he proposed to her on the night he died - while his enduring and committed love for his two young sons, Tom and Freddie, brought Hunt great pleasure.

The press and sporting public may have had their own opinions and ideas about who James was, but to those two young men he was simply "dad".

And, as a result of that, they can give a unique - if an all too sadly brief - insight into the James Hunt who lived outside the spotlight.

"He loved mowing the lawn," eldest son Tom says, grinning - while helping confirm that Hunt could master anything with a petrol engine.

"He was really passionate about that.

"The stripes had to be perfect, he had an old fashioned one that you would do tennis courts with.

"I've not got that many memories, to be honest. He took us for walks on Wimbledon Common, took us to football matches and at home he took a lot of time for his budgies. We had an aviary with around 250 on them.

HE HAD CHARISMA AND IT CAME NATURALLY TO HIM. IT WAS NOTHING THAT YOU COULD TRY TO DESIGN OR MAKE UP. HE WAS HIS OWN MAN

"He also loved playing snooker and he was always super competitive about golf, squash and tennis. It was always individual sports. He spent hours at the snooker table with Jimmy White and Roger Waters of Pink Floyd. Apparently, he gave Jimmy some close games.

"One of my favourite stories involves a £100 bet he had with a friend about who'd get 100 points first.

"Dad scored 98 at his first visit to the table and his opponent conceded there and then.

"But to us he was just dad."

Freddie – whose resemblance to his father can often stop you in your tracks – concurs that Hunt might have been many things to many people but most of all, and most importantly, he was a bright and loving father, no different to anyone else.

However, Hunt's well-known tendency to get himself into a scrape of some sort or other also seems to have been a theme.

"I remember a day when he set the silver birch alight, that is one of my vivid memories," Freddie laughs.

"He had a bonfire at the bottom of the garden and it was so big that the silver birch went black for years afterwards. I must've been really young – two or three, I

suppose – but I definitely remember that!"

Tom was just seven and Freddie a little over 12 months younger when their father passed away, a shattering blow for any young person, and the two remain extremely proud of James, his 1976 triumph and the way he continues to capture the public's imagination.

Freddie said: "It's fantastic and it's very flattering that people remember him well, still love him – and it is equally, if not more, flattering that the younger generation also seem to regard him extremely highly."

"It's amazing, really," Tom concurred. "You grow up with him as your dad as a kid and now all this interest is incredible."

So why does Hunt remain such a captivating figure?

There have been both longer and more successful careers, yet the name "James Hunt" invokes far stronger emotions – and far bigger smiles – than many modern-day careers.

"I think it is because what you saw was what you got," Tom said. "He had such a unique approach to racing. His stats on paper, compared to other drivers, are not that much to write home about, but the

ABOVE: James, Sarah, Tom and Freddie

"THE TABLOID IMAGE IS SOMETHING THAT WAS HIM. BUT HE DIDN'T JUST PARTY ALL NIGHT AND THEN GET INTO A CAR"

way he went about his racing made him popular with a lot of people.

"He had charisma and it came naturally to him. It was nothing that you could try to design or make up, and he certainly had it. People warmed to him and he warmed to them. Dad had a certain kind of coolness that isn't around now. He was his own man. But he had to be. How else would he have got away with going to a black-tie event in bare feet?"

Freddie added: "He comes across to many people as the reckless playboy, but that wasn't really the case. He was very serious and professional – although there is no denying that he certainly knew how to let his hair down and have fun.

"But even when he was being serious, his personality made it fun. From mowing the lawn to the bird breeding."

Being the son of James Hunt – particularly in light of some fairly sensational claims about his playboy days at the height of his fame, including sleeping with 5,000 women – could prompt some embarrassment.

All those who knew James best claimed that he well and truly enjoyed himself with the opposite sex and although Tom and Freddie in no way disagree with that, they like to add a touch of perspective to proceedings.

"I'm sure if he said it he was saying it in jest," Tom said. "But there is no doubt that was part of him and everyone loved him because of it. The tabloid image is

Freddie and Tom, with mum Sarah and grandmother Rosie Lomax, outside the Celebration of the Life of James Hunt service, held at St James's Church, Piccadilly, London, in September 1993

something that was him. But he didn't just party all night and then get into a car. I went through some of the handwritten notes he made after some of his earlier races, which were really interesting. They showed how meticulous he was about the car and racing."

Freddie, in particular, has embraced his father's legacy – and driving instinct – by also becoming a racing driver.

He has begun competing in the NASCAR Whelen Euro Series, with his ultimate goal being to win the Le Mans 24-hour race – arguably the most gruelling and famous race on the planet.

"When I first started driving I loved the idea of becoming an Formula One driver and emulating dad and becoming world champion, but it didn't take long to realise that with my lack of experience and suitable lack of funding that would not happen," he said.

"The only hope I had of doing it was to get really well funded season after season to get the miles under my belt. Now I just want to make a nice career out of driving."

Freddie's own career and experiences have helped give a unique perspective on both Hunt the man and Hunt the driver.

He has driven his dad's Hesketh 308 on several occasions and is more respectful than ever about the risks involved in a 1970s racing career.

During Hunt's time in Formula One, there were seven driver fatalities, including his good friend Ronnie Peterson, who Hunt had courageously helped drag out of his burning Lotus 78 at the 1978 Italian Grand Prix.

" HE HAD A LOT OF INTEGRITY AND DID EVERYTHING TO THE BEST OF HIS ABILITY. THAT IS SOMETHING TO ADMIRE "

"They were tremendously brave men," Freddie said. "I've driven dad's cars a couple of times now and they were tremendously dangerous. When I drive them I have to remind myself that we're not in a high-tech carbon-fibre car frame. If you crashed in those cars they were not much fun at all.

"Also, your own driving could be absolutely perfect but you could suffer mechanical failure and, again, face serious trouble. Suspension or engine trouble could hit at any time and as a driver you had to put that to the back of your mind.

"What dad did was calculate the risk before the season or before each race and then decide whether you wanted to take that risk so that, when you got in that car, you had already accepted the risk and you just got on with it.

"I have tremendous admiration for all the drivers as a result. Dad was very safety conscious; that was why he retired early. He had won his World Championship and he wanted to get out alive."

Hunt did indeed get out alive, although his death prevented him from passing on his lawn mowing and budgie breeding tips to his sons.

However, it is quite clear that the years which have passed since Hunt's death have done nothing to diminish their love and respect for the man they simply called "dad".

"He had a lot of integrity, he was determined to succeed and did everything to the best of his ability," Freddie said.

"That is something to respect, remember and admire."

> **MY INVOLVEMENT IN FORMULA ONE THESE DAYS GIVES ME A DIFFERENT ENJOYMENT. I'VE BEEN WORKING WITH MURRAY WALKER FOR MORE THAN 10 YEARS. HE'S SUCH FUN AND SUCH AN ENTHUSIAST**

Hunt on the BBC

> **I RECKON I'D HAD A FAIR CRACK OF THE WHIP. THE MAIN THING WAS SELF-PRESERVATION**

Hunt on retiring

> **IT DIDN'T BOTHER ME BECAUSE I TOLD MYSELF IT WAS A NATURAL RHYME AND NOT NECESSARILY AN ASPERSION SO I COULD EASE THE PAIN**

Hunt on his "Hunt the Shunt" nickname

> **THE TIMES WHEN I WAS ACTUALLY SICK BEFORE GETTING INTO A CAR WERE MORE IN MY FORMULA THREE DAYS. THAT WAS JUST THE TENSION AND NERVES. I WAS PERMANENTLY UNDER TREMENDOUS PRESSURE BECAUSE IF ANYTHING HAPPENED TO THE CAR I HAD TO PAY FOR IT**

Hunt on being sick before a race

" I TOOK ONE LOOK AND SAID, 'THAT'S FOR ME. IF HE CAN DO IT, THERE'S NO REASON WHY I CAN'T' "

Hunt on falling in love with racing

" THEY WERE LUCKY BECAUSE, UNEXPECTEDLY, IT STOPPED RAINING. IT HARDLY RAINED AT ALL DURING THE RACE. IN FACT, THE SUN CAME OUT AND THAT REALLY WAS A PROBLEM BECAUSE IT WAS SO LOW. YOU COULDN'T SEE A THING "

Hunt on the 1976 Japan Grand Prix

" I SAID I WAS DRIVING THE THING. I WENT OUT AND ON MY FIRST FLYING LAP GOT THE FIRST POLE OF MY CAREER. THAT IMPRESSED THE BOYS, OF COURSE. THEY LIKE CHARGERS AND THEY'D SEEN ME STAND UP TO TEDDY MAYER. AFTER THAT, I WAS VERY MUCH NO.1 "

Hunt on setting the standards at McLaren

" RACING DRIVERS, LIKE TENNIS PLAYERS AND OTHER SPORTS STARS, SEEM TO ATTRACT THE MOST BEAUTIFUL WOMEN IN THE WORLD. AND, OF COURSE, THERE'S PLENTY OF ROOM FOR THEM TO SIT AROUND THE CIRCUIT LOOKING STUNNING AND PRETENDING TO BE WORKING A STOPWATCH "

Hunt on his sex appeal